SEVENTEENTH IN A SERIES
ANNUAL PUBLIC DISCUSSIONS
ON PROBLEMS OF CURRENT INTEREST
IN THE SOCIAL SCIENCES AND THE HUMANITIES

MAN
VS.
TIME

CO-MODERATORS: ROBERT S. HOYT
LEONID HURWICZ

SALLY PRATT
EDITOR

ANN MAUCKER
ASSISTANT EDITOR

Presented and Published Under the Auspices of the
GRADUATE SCHOOL RESEARCH CENTER
in cooperation with the GENERAL EXTENSION DIVISION
University of Minnesota
Minneapolis, Minnesota 55455

Foreword

This series of programs originated in a discussion among members of the Graduate School Advisory Council for the Social Sciences. It was agreed that the emphasis in this year's series should be on the nature of the social sciences as academic disciplines rather than on the ways in which these disciplines are useful or find application in society. A discussion of the techniques and methods used by scholars in the social sciences was one way to accomplish this purpose, but the Council thought that this sort of discussion would tend to be so technical that the programs would present a limited appeal to the audience we wanted to reach. As an alternative to a series on methodology, it was then decided to discuss an important factor common to all the social sciences.

The factor we selected was *time*—the ways in which *time* influences, limits, extends, or must be taken into account by the various social sciences, whether in the acquisition of knowledge, the evaluation of data, or the process of making generalizations. It was further agreed that, since time is equally a factor in disciplines outside the social sciences, some attention should be given to the natural sciences and the humanities in order to illustrate further, both by comparison and by contrast, the nature of the social sciences.

Contents

MAN VS. TIME: INTRODUCTION   1
CO-MODERATORS ROBERT S. HOYT, PROFESSOR OF HISTORY
LEONID HURWICZ, PROFESSOR OF ECONOMICS
DAVID COOPERMAN, PROFESSOR AND CHAIRMAN OF THE SOCIAL SCIENCE PROGRAM

TIME AT THE DAWN OF HISTORY   11
WILLIAM A. MCDONALD, PROFESSOR OF CLASSICS AND DIRECTOR OF THE HONORS PROGRAM
HERBERT E. WRIGHT, JR., PROFESSOR OF GEOLOGY AND DIRECTOR OF THE LIMNOLOGICAL RESEARCH CENTER
MISS DIANNE M. BORCHERT, UNIVERSITY SENIOR MAJORING IN SPEECH AND THEATRE ARTS
MRS. ELEANOR FENTON, PROFESSOR AND ASSISTANT TO THE DEAN OF THE GENERAL EXTENSION DIVISION

TIME AND SOCIOLOGICAL CHANGE   35
ROY G. FRANCIS, PROFESSOR OF SOCIOLOGY
DOUGLAS M. HEAD, MINNEAPOLIS ATTORNEY AND FORMER STATE LEGISLATOR
DONAL M. MORRISON, MINNEAPOLIS *Star* COLUMNIST

TICK TOCK TROUBLES   51
GEORGE D. FREIER, PROFESSOR OF PHYSICS
MRS. PATRICIA COLLINS, WIFE OF THE CHAIRMAN OF THE ELECTRICAL ENGINEERING DEPARTMENT
WALTER TRENERRY, ST. PAUL ATTORNEY AND PRESIDENT OF THE MCKNIGHT FOUNDATION

TIME AND HUMAN KNOWLEDGE   75
D. BURNHAM TERRELL, PROFESSOR OF PHILOSOPHY
ROBERT H. BECK, PROFESSOR OF THE HISTORY AND PHILOSOPHY OF EDUCATION
BRYCE CRAWFORD, JR., PROFESSOR OF CHEMISTRY AND DEAN OF THE GRADUATE SCHOOL

TIME AND THE SCIENCE OF MAN   91
ROBERT F. SPENCER, PROFESSOR OF ANTHROPOLOGY
MRS. BARBARA CUNNINGHAM, CHAIRMAN OF THE BROOKLYN CENTER HUMAN RELATIONS COMMITTEE AND SECRETARY OF THE COMMITTEE OF CONCERN
O. MEREDITH WILSON, PRESIDENT OF THE UNIVERSITY OF MINNESOTA

TIME AND SPACE IN BAROQUE ARCHITECTURE 105

HYLTON A. THOMAS, PROFESSOR OF ART

WALTER W. HELLER, PROFESSOR OF ECONOMICS AND FORMER CHAIRMAN OF THE PRESIDENT'S COUNCIL OF ECONOMIC ADVISORS

LESLIE MACFARLANE, VISITING PROFESSOR OF HISTORY AT MACALESTER COLLEGE

TIME, TIMING AND TIMELINESS 129

ROY E. CARTER, PROFESSOR OF JOURNALISM AND SOCIOLOGY AND DIRECTOR OF THE SCHOOL OF JOURNALISM COMMUNICATION RESEARCH DIVISION

ROBERT COURSEN, EDITOR OF THE MINNEAPOLIS Tribune's MINNESOTA POLL

ROY G. FRANCIS, PROFESSOR OF SOCIOLOGY

PAUL A. GILJE, DIRECTOR OF RESEARCH AND PUBLICATIONS FOR THE CITIZEN'S LEAGUE OF MINNEAPOLIS AND HENNEPIN COUNTY

E. W. ZIEBARTH, DEAN OF THE UNIVERSITY'S COLLEGE OF LIBERAL ARTS

CRITICAL TIMES AND BEHAVIOR CHANGE 147

MRS. ELAINE C. WALSTER, ASSOCIATE PROFESSOR OF PSYCHOLOGY AND IN THE OFFICE OF THE DEAN OF STUDENTS

JOHN C. WRIGHT, ASSOCIATE PROFESSOR IN THE INSTITUTE OF CHILD DEVELOPMENT

MRS. DOROTHY LEWIS, ST. PAUL Dispatch REPORTER

HOMER E. MASON, ASSOCIATE PROFESSOR OF PHILOSOPHY

ECONOMICS: TIME DIMENSION 159

O. H. BROWNLEE, PROFESSOR AND CHAIRMAN OF ECONOMICS

JOHN R. BORCHERT, PROFESSOR OF GEOGRAPHY

CLEMENT UDEZE (NIGERIA), GRADUATE STUDENT IN HISTORY

TIME AND THE SIGNIFICANCE OF POLITICS 175

MULFORD Q. SIBLEY, PROFESSOR OF POLITICAL SCIENCE

FRANK ADAMS, STATE SENATOR

WAYNE G. POPHAM, STATE SENATOR

TIME, CHANGE AND PERIODIZATION IN HISTORY 191

JOHN B. WOLF, PROFESSOR OF HISTORY

WILLIAM G. SHEPHERD, UNIVERSITY VICE PRESIDENT FOR ACADEMIC ADMINISTRATION

GERHARD H. WEISS, ASSOCIATE PROFESSOR OF GERMAN

Man vs. Time: Introduction

How do historians and other social scientists cope with time?

CO-MODERATORS: *ROBERT S. HOYT*, PROFESSOR OF HISTORY
LEONID HURWICZ, PROFESSOR OF ECONOMICS

SPEAKER: *DAVID COOPERMAN*, PROFESSOR AND CHAIRMAN OF THE
SOCIAL SCIENCE PROGRAM

Professor Hoyt: For this television series our thought was to find an interesting factor common to all the social sciences. The one we selected pervades all disciplines. During the next twelve weeks we shall concern ourselves with the factor of time as it influences the social science disciplines and also other disciplines, in the humanities and natural sciences, as they serve to illustrate problems in the social sciences.

There are many ways in which time is taken into account as a factor limiting or sometimes extending the acquisition of knowledge in the social sciences. Perhaps the most obvious way, to an historian, is that a sequence of events over a period of time forms the substance of our discipline. There are many other factors. I would like to ask Professor Hurwicz and Professor Cooperman to indicate briefly some of the main factors.

Professor Cooperman: It would seem at first glance that speculation by social scientists about changes in human transactions would simply be a matter of developing increasingly refined techniques for observing more minute moments of time progressions. After all, the story of progress in the natural sciences would appear to be the story of the development of finer instruments of measurement, such as chronometers. However, in both the natural and the social sciences there is a more significant aspect of progress in acquiring knowledge about reality. Research in the history of the sciences reveals that the conceptions of time themselves demonstrate development or change. The history of ideas of time among social scientists and theorists suggests that such views played an important part in shaping the course of human events themselves, especially during the nineteenth century.

Professor Hurwicz: Time forms the great framework for analysis in many of the fields. As an economist I think in particular of such problems in economics as business cycle development models, but the question of the basic conceptual framework is something we want to hear more about. Karl Pearson's *Grammar of Science* deals with this subject, and I would be interested to have your reaction to it, Professor Cooperman. Pearson says: "Like space, time appears to us as one of the plans on which the great sorting machine of human perceptive faculty arranges its material." Is that a natural way to think of time from your point of view?

Cooperman: It is natural, but not therefore accurate, or even helpful. Ordinarily, or naturally, we tend to think of time as an object itself. This is implied in the quotation from Pearson and is illustrated by the response of many people to a question like, "What does a metronome do?" A metronome, as far as musicians and listeners are concerned, measures time. But which time—whose time? In the case of music, a little analysis suggests that metronomic time is not "natural" but is created by the composer. Musical notation is divided by the "creator" into moments of varying meter and rhythm. The closest analogy to thinking about human time is the Judaeo-Christian view of history, which holds that God intervenes to order human history into epochs which have divine meaning. And yet, even to profound and intelligent religious minds the idea of time has seemed shrouded in mystery. In the fifth century A.D., St. Augustine asked the question, "What then is time?" And he responded, "If no one asked me, I know what it is. If I wish to explain it to him who asks, I know not."

We should try to unravel such paradoxes by making distinctions between instruments for specific human time purposes, such as metronomes and clocks on the one hand, and statements about absolute time dimensions on the other.

Hurwicz: In several weeks a guest physicist will tell us what he thinks of clocks. I am not sure whether he will think of them as a communication device, but we will find out then.

Cooperman: In my opinion, the social sciences at this stage of development are at pre-Einsteinian levels with respect to constructing a general theory of social change.

Social scientists must consider the philosophical significance of some basic questions about time—questions which were raised in the natural sciences by Sir Isaac Newton in this famous work, *Principia Mathematica.* "True" time, according to Newton, appears to be an inherent aspect of physical reality, which is measured by clock devices. Two questions might be raised about this view. Firstly, from the standpoint of modern physics, this view has been criticized as being too absolutistic. The twentieth-century physicist Ernst Mach suggested: "It is beyond our power to measure the changes of things by time. On the contrary, time is an abstraction at which we arrive because things and human behavior appear to change." That is, time itself is a human construction which we apply to whatever physical reality may be in order to derive interpretations or explanations of that reality. Secondly, concerning personal relationships, the French philosopher, Henri Bergson, interpreted conceptions of time even more flexibly and openly than did Mach. Like Newton, he suggested the term "duration" may be a useful name for time—but he meant it in a different sense than Newton. Bergson's view might be called "private time." That is, the moments of measurement for individuals and society should be the memorable instances of humans. People might measure their lives according to private events such as "my first day at school," "my first communion," "my wedding day," and so on. Of course unless all individuals in a population share the same sequence of private events with at least somewhat similar intervals between the events, it would be difficult for the members to "measure" time accurately for scientific purposes. But several notable anthropologists have described how primitive societies manage very well on a shared conception of social-personal time.

The above remarks help to clarify the possible meanings of time. I hope they also indicate that changes in human relationships can be described without ever using the term "time." In fact if we are very skeptical about any *absolute* sense of that word we may be able to predict and explain aggregate human behavior better without using "time" in many sentences. I wonder if Professor Hurwicz would like to consider this question?

Hurwicz: Well, most of us, as soon as we hear the term *predict*, think that almost by definition we are in a framework of time. But it is true that in certain fields of analysis, particularly in economics, people sometimes try to get around the notion of analyzing phenomena over time. We talk about something called comparative studies. Actually, this is not as mysterious as one might think. One can say the tendency among economists in recent years—perhaps even decades— has been to pay attention to how things move from one position of equilibrium to another, partly because it is interesting to know. Some people view the whole process of the business cycle as a disturbance away from equilibrium. There are many people who question whether we ever have a chance—especially in this turbulent era—to observe the equilibrium position. If we do not study, a little bit at least, the way things behave when they are away from equilibrium, you might not get very close to the description of the reality in which we live.

Cooperman: I should imagine, however, that we might be able to express some economic relationships, just as we express any generalization of a scientific nature, in terms which are literally "timeless." The so-called law of supply and demand says something like "if supply factors rise in relation to demand factors then always—other things being equal—prices will fall." There is an implication in that statement concerning future action, but it still makes perfect sense if we speak about a succession of supply-demand relationships rather than refer to an absolute conception of time.

Hurwicz: I was about to make a comment along those lines. One thing that scientists have learned—not only social scientists, but also physical scientists in this era of quantum theory—is that you are much safer stating probabilities, or saying that a certain event is more likely to take place in one way than the other. Actually, this does not mean that we necessarily deny that the present and past—if we knew them with complete accuracy—do determine the future. Of course, we never know the present and the past with complete accuracy. If we want to be realistic, we have to allow for a great many variables that are important. Probably the best we can say is that in a large class of cases, if the supply of a certain commodity should go up while demand conditions remain the same, then there will be some kind of an adjustment movement, something that is similar to the kind of wiggles we see on the chart of the stock market every day in the paper.

Cooperman: Even concerning stock market behavior, I believe it would be valuable for someone interested in profit-making to know about the behavior of the stock of one company in relation to that of competitors. If this is what is important in the economic market place, then again I would suggest that a relative conception of time may be very adequate.

Hurwicz: Is it not true some people think that professors are like that too, that they have a relative notion of time.

3

Cooperman: Yes, but relative notions of time, I have been trying to say, can be very helpful. We remember events because we can relate them to other patterns of events in the past. For example, a parent might ask a child, "Do you remember the time when you were small and such and such happened?" And the child may respond, "Oh, I remember now. That happened when we lived at 120 Jones Street and I was in second grade. I must have been seven years old."

Hence, the important point is that if there is some clear memory of sequential relations, that may be all that time "means."

Hurwicz: Of course, you would not want to rely on the sequence being quite right.

Cooperman: That is correct. We have invented devices such as clocks to help us remember sequential orders. But such devices often end by imposing their particular metric notions of time on the social order itself. Many writers have claimed that human life has been fragmented and atomized by such metric devices. It seems to be true, if paradoxical, that clocks and similar instruments, which begin as convenient tools, end by being considered the very definition of time itself. This also illustrates the way in which the very fabric of societies are changed by socially derived devices themselves.

Hurwicz: Some people find it inconvenient. This occurs to me because I remember about a group of people from a South Pacific island who were evacuated in connection with a volcanic explosion there. They were taken to London to live in presumed opulence and comfort. After about a year or two they asked to be taken back to their primitive and very uncomfortable little volcanic island because they did not have to get up at seven o'clock every morning.

Cooperman: To summarize, social scientists do not study absolute time, but changes in aggregate or individual human behavior. For the sake of convenience, calendar time periods may be chosen as a context for comparison. For example, economists interested in the study of national income have more or less agreed to use yearly accounting systems. It is true, on the other hand, that there creeps into the work of some social scientists a view that time itself is the object of study.

Hurwicz: You mean they are, somehow, making a big fuss about it? You mean they treat it as if it were a material object?

Cooperman: Yes, exactly. One well-known and respected sociologist recently wrote as follows: "Without time there is no change." That statement might be of interest to a metaphysician; but it is of no use to a social scientist.

Hurwicz: In fact you wonder if anyone has tried living without time. How would they know?

Cooperman: The answer seems simple to me. Without *change* there is no sense of time. I am reminded of Pearson's interpretation of time. He said, "at the very least there must be recurring cycles as a basis for marking of units of time . . . time like space, sets limits on human life." I do believe we can accept the idea that humans establish certain convenient time limitations. But you see how easy it is to treat those conveniences as if they were absolute poles of existence. Examine the very title of this television series: "Time vs. Man." It appears as if there are two separate units—one, Man, and two, Time. The misleading implications of this way of putting the subject should be obvious.

Hurwicz: Are you suggesting that when you have this heading "Man vs. Time," you really have men on both sides of the fight?

Cooperman: Well, there is no fight involved.

Hurwicz: I am disappointed.

Cooperman: Let me turn to changing conceptions of and theories about time. Certainly, "from the beginning of time," to coin a phrase, men have thought about the ways in which civilization has changed. The ancient Greeks wrote about cycles of civilization. The seventeenth century Italian historian, Giambattista Vico, wrote about eternal recurrences in the history of western civilization. What was implied in some of these writings was that there is an almost "wired-in" sequence of events which runs as follows: If a society is observed in its democratic phase, it can be foretold that the society will soon become aristocratic in its political base. Then a dictatorship will invariably follow and finally the society will return to its democratic origins, to begin over again.

Hurwicz: We probably know some examples exactly according to that sequence.

Cooperman: However, once such a theory was stated in that form, individuals behaved as if that were the only way humans could change, thus tending to fulfill what were, after all, crude human forecasts. At the time of the American Revolution several notable leaders read the events of '76 as part of a recurrent cycle of civilization.

Hurwicz: Was this an idea that this was really inevitable, that no matter how one tries to head it off—it's like in a Greek tragedy—it is bound to . . .

Cooperman: Exactly. These views began to change in the past two centuries. In the period of thought called the "Enlightenment" it was suggested that over any sequence of events, progress in human affairs is inevitable. Sequential order itself inevitably is unilinear on an upward slope.

A variation of this view was developed by some thinkers in the nineteenth century. Now, it is asserted, human society develops in stages, also invariably upwards. Both Karl Marx and the founder of sociology, Auguste Comte, shared this view. Marx, for example, held that before human society began to be complex there was no change. Rather life was very much as it was in the Garden of Eden before Adam's fall.

Hurwicz: You are not implying that Marx was taking a page out of the Bible in this respect?

Cooperman: Without realizing it, I think he was. After some division of labor, according to him, change begins to occur and history, in Marx's sense, begins. It continues progressively as classes conflict with one another until it ends with the victory of the proletariat. At that point, with the appearance of Communist society, history, change, and time, cease for all social purposes.

Other, more recent thinkers assert that there is progress in human societies, but it occurs unevenly. Changes may occur slowly at first but the rate itself increases after a while. Some variations on this theme suggest that in the short run apparent retrogression occurs, but such moments give way to general progress when measured over the long run.

Another way time has been depicted is by conceiving of the development of civilization as upward movement, but at uneven rates. Civilizations grow along on the upward slope of a line. This view holds that human changes occur at first slowly and then speed up and "snowball uphill" until we are at the dawn of large-scale improvements. These improvements tend to slow down every so often only in preparation for the next big push upward.

Another way of putting it is like the way in which some economic historians and economists have depicted business cycles. There is a peak and valley kind of behavior at certain stages over time. A line can be drawn that represents the average movements of the apparently "unlawful" trends.

Hurwicz: Next week we shall discuss some of the various parts of the history of Greece. I think we will have an example of very definite retrogression. A situation in which, at one time, the Greeks already had some writing and other earmarks of civilization. Then because of invasions, or for other reasons, they really sank back to a much lower level. It took quite a bit of time to get back to the level of civilization they had reached several hundred years earlier. I suppose others might view the Middle Ages in this light.

Cooperman: As we observe more recent interpretations of time we can see that the views become more open-ended than the first interpretations. One conception of cultural development might be termed a theory of branching evolution. If we choose to draw a vertical line at any place on a graph and then ask "what possibilities are given for developments which succeed this point of time?", we can infer that certain trends are possible, certain others are excluded, or highly unlikely.

Hurwicz: Does this correspond, for instance, to the idea when you analyze the developments of present-day India? People would say: well, if they are able to solve such and such economic problem, if they learn to cope with the food shortage, then they might be able to develop their industry relatively rapidly; on the other hand, if they do not manage to do it, there may be a period of industrial stagnation for the next fifty years. And this question, whether they will do this first thing or the second, we might not really have any basis for determining; although, we might, for instance, think that they are more likely to plunge into industrial development, but we certainly could not guarantee it.

Cooperman: There are also two other examples of social scientific depictions of time. These do not refer to large, multi-valued factors, but to comparatively simple developments of correlations of changes. First, is a simple population growth chart for some cultures. Population grows slowly at first and then the rate of change increases logarithmically.

Hurwicz: Professor Cooperman, is it not true that if we had to place ourselves on such a curve, we would be on a very steep part of it right now? There is some argument as to whether it will level off.

Cooperman: Yes. Secondly, there are exponential growth curves, which might be drawn for types of inventions in industrial societies. You can clearly see how changes in social patterns can be measured rather than any absolute temporary idea.

Hurwicz: There is one point I think that typically occurs to us when we consider various theories of development over time. Somehow someone gets the impression that it is time that is causing the development, whether in a deterministic way or some more vague manner. Of course, this may have been the idea at some point in the past when we thought the Golden Age was followed by the Silver and Bronze Age and so on. I think now we realize that what each historical period does is to create a certain situation, which may be regarded its fruit; but in turn, it becomes the seed for the next period. I think the basic task of the social scientist is really to see how these events, that occur in time, are related to one another. Today grows out of yesterday and tomorrow out of today. It is true that when somebody else later looks at it, he can show us how things developed over time. And, of course, the person who typically picks up those pieces is the historian. It seems to me that it is quite natural to put him on the spot at this point and have him straighten us out.

Cooperman: Heaven, indeed, forbid that.

Hoyt: The wide-ranging remarks we have just heard from Professor Cooperman illustrate, in many ways, the application or pertinence of time to several social-science fields. If we consider the ways in which time has been a factor in history, practically every way in which time influences one or another of the social sciences has to be dealt with by historians. One factor that is particularly interesting is the way in which historians are influenced by the environment of their own age in interpreting the past.

Possibly the most extreme example of this is the so-called Whig interpretation of history. This is a way of looking at the past which, in its ultimate origins, did have something to do with the triumph of the Whig Party in the late seventeenth century in England, but which, as developed in the course of the nineteenth century by the great historians of that period, is associated not with just Whigs or politics, but rather as a way in which professional historians of all political persuasions looked at the past. The example that I like to cite as an obvious example is the good Bishop of Oxford, William Stubbs. He was by no means a liberal or a Whig; he was indeed a high Tory. This Whig interpretation of history, as it is referred to, is not to be identified with any liberal view of the past. It has three marked characteristics.

One is the tendency to transfer from the present into the past the value system of the present. It is the tendency to consider those things to be important for a remote period of time which are important in the generation of the historian who is writing. Stubbs, for example, wrote a three-volume *Constitutional History of England* which is largely a commentary on the growth of parliament. This is the central, over-riding theme.

Another characteristic of Whig interpretation of the past, again, illustrates the element of value judgment, that is, the emphasis upon progress as something which is exhibited through time in unbroken continuity. Everything in the past makes its little contribution toward the culmination of history in the day in which the historian is living. The growth of parliament, for example, is traced back beyond the actual meetings of institutions called parliament in the thirteenth century. Indeed, the remote ancestor of the modern Victorian parliament of Stubbs' day is the tribal assembly of the Teutonic forests. And this is described almost as if it were a House of Commons session.

Finally, a tendency—again illustrating the use of value judgment in the Whig interpretation of history—is to denominate everything as either good or bad; that is, your measuring stick is whether an event does or does not contribute toward the moral and political, also the economic and institutional, system which is the Golden Age in which we today are living. If it does, then it is good; if it does not, of course, it is bad. Of course, in this connection one thinks of the classic take-off or caricature of the Whig interpretation of history, the book entitled *1066 and All That,* in which the whole sequence of events, panoramically viewed, is divided up into things that are good and things that are bad.

Hurwicz: That is about England. Is there anything like that for the United States, like *1776 and All That?*

Hoyt: I wish there were. I have not seen one yet, but certainly an example is the way George Washington has been treated in American history until forty or fifty years ago. This would certainly illustrate the general view of the past that was so characteristic of a group of professional historians in England.

One other facet of this interpretation is that any quick change, any revolutionary change, is, above all, a bad thing. Progress is not the result of human reason upsetting and overthrowing the established order. The established order must change slowly and gradually in accordance with the common-sense notions of the Anglo-Saxon inheritance. Well, I could expand this to great lengths and go into details of the view of the past which is called Whig interpretation of history, but the main point is that the time in which the historian lives is going to affect his view of the past. He can either be a slave of his own time, which I think most of the Whig historians were, or he can intelligently recognize the influence of his own day upon his value judgments, upon his distinguishing the important from less important things in the past. Having consciously made this distinction, the historian should try to determine the influence of his own day on his view of the past and make allowances for it. He would not claim that history is a pure science. Objectivity of history will never, of course, be completely achieved.

Cooperman: I recall one of the strongest ironies about the Whig interpretation of history. As late as 1913, J. B. Bury said: "The struggle of reason against authority has ended in what appears to be a decisive and permanent victory for liberty . . . Victory is permanent; intelligent freedom is now assured to mankind as a possession forever."[1]

Hoyt: It was World War I which jolted the historians out of their complacency and first cast doubt upon the Whig interpretation. It is still alive in some textbooks, but these views of history are now pretty much passé among professional historians.

J. Wesley Smith, in the well-known cartoon series,[2] is a good example of this. The element of anachronism is delightfully portrayed in this classic cartoon

---

[1] *A History of the Freedom of Thought* (London, Oxford University Press, 1913), p. 246.

[2] Burr Shafer, *Through History with J. Wesley Smith* (New York: Vanguard Press, Inc., 1950). Reproduced by permission. Copyright, 1950, 1960, by Burr Shafer.

"Bread and circuses! Bread and circuses! What I want is Social Security."

"It's a new unemployment project—Rameses calls it a pyramid."

where the gentleman is made to exclaim: "Bread and circuses! Bread and circuses! What I want is Social Security."

Hurwicz: Medicare too, probably.

Hoyt: Or, for example: "It's a new unemployment project—Rameses calls it a pyramid."[3]

In other words, this tendency to interpret the past in terms of the present results only in distorting the past in terms of the evidence critically examined.

---

[3] *Ibid.*

Time at the Dawn of History

How did it all begin?

SPEAKERS: *WILLIAM A. McDONALD*, PROFESSOR OF CLASSICS AND DIRECTOR OF THE HONORS PROGRAM
HERBERT C. WRIGHT, PROFESSOR OF GEOLOGY AND DIRECTOR OF THE LIMNOLOGICAL RESEARCH CENTER

COMMENTATORS: *MRS. ELEANOR FENTON*, PROFESSOR AND ASSISTANT TO THE DEAN OF THE GENERAL EXTENSION DIVISION
MISS DIANNE M. BORCHERT, UNIVERSITY SENIOR MAJORING IN SPEECH AND THEATRE ARTS

Professor Hurwicz: Man vs. Time. This is the historian's bread-and-butter. Who is more qualified than an historian to give us an answer to the universal question: "How did it all begin?"

Professor McDonald, the topic we are discussing refers to the dawn of history, the dawn of time. When most of us think of early periods we often think of what we studied in high school, and in particular, of the Homeric period, which

is almost as early as they come, but mostly we think about myth, fantasy, stories of gods flying about. For instance, I remember a picture that one sees in Virgil's *Aeneid* which shows the burning of Troy and Aeneas[1] carrying out his father as a first step towards the foundation of the empire of Rome many hundreds of years later. What does the modern historian have to tell us about this?

Professor McDonald: Opinion has changed a good deal over the centuries, Professor Hurwicz. In the days of the classical Greeks themselves, Homer was history; Homer was the bible. They believed that he had been there and knew all about the Trojan war and the rest. They even decided boundary disputes by referring to Homer.

Hurwicz: That shows a high degree of confidence!

McDonald: It was too high. Well, in relatively modern times, most people did not believe that Homer had *any* historical basis for his poems, the *Iliad* and the *Odyssey*. Some of them even questioned whether he had ever existed—and so they tended not to believe Homer. They felt that he used his imagination. This continued up to about one hundred years ago. Then we started to get modern archeology, modern excavation—not very modern, perhaps at first—but soon we had something definite to cope with, for instance, the walls of Troy.

Fortification of Troy VI, outer face, from the southeast in 1937.[2]

---

[1] Publius Virgilius Marco, *The Works of Virgil.* Translated by John Dryden. (London: Jacob Tonson, 1697), p. 263.

[2] Carl W. Blegen, John L. Caskey, and Marion Rawson, *Troy: The Sixth Settlement,* v. III, part 2 (Princeton University Press, 1953), plate 19. Reprinted by permission. Copyright 1953, by Princeton University Press.

Hurwicz: Do you have any reasons for thinking that we actually know where the city of Troy was?

McDonald: Yes, I think that most people would agree now that we do know where Homer's Troy was. And we can go on to more modern excavation in other places where we not only have the walls, but enough evidence so that we can reconstruct a palace. I believe that if Agamemnon saw the reconstruction that has been recently been made of his palace, he would not be completely lost; he would, perhaps, recognize where this was.

Hurwicz: What period are we talking about?

Reconstruction of Agamemnon's Palace which was built about the 14th century B.C. Surrounded by the fertile Argive plain, the huge limestone citadel was enclosed by walls estimated to be 20 to 25 feet thick and up to 60 feet high.[3]

---

[3] *The Epic of Man,* Editors of *Life* (New York: Time Incorporated, 1961), pp. 152-53. Reprinted by permission. Copyright, 1961, by Time, Incorporated. Drawn by Alton S. Tobey.

McDonald: This is what we call the Mycenaean Age.

Hurwicz: Mycenaean? What does that refer to?

McDonald: The name comes from the town of Mycenae. We can see its location. It might be well to check a little bit on early Greek geography.

Here we have Mycenae, the biggest and most powerful town of the whole area. It was the capital; it was the place where the expedition against Troy was

organized. You can perhaps orient yourself by seeing Athens and Sparta, which are better known in more modern times but were also Mycenaean sites.

Hurwicz: Now, of the personages one remembers from Homer, one very famous name is that of Nestor. Can you locate him anywhere?

McDonald: Yes. Nestor lived at Pylos, which is shown down in the southwest corner. This is one of the most recently discovered citadels of Mycenaean kings and this one I have had some connection with myself. It is interesting that each of these capitals was the administrative center of a quite large kingdom, far larger than classical city-states. The University of Minnesota has an expedition that has been exploring this area around Pylos, and we have found the location of over 125 towns and villages which once belonged to Nestor's kingdom.

Hurwicz: All are in that area around Pylos? Then Homer was not exaggerating when he indicated that this was quite an impressive area.

McDonald: These were big kingdoms. Homer says these kingdoms—some 30 of them—controlled most of central and southern Greece. They also had widespread trade relations with the whole eastern Mediterranean, westward to Sicily, up to Troy, and down to Crete, Egypt and the Syrian coast.

Hurwicz: Troy would be near Constantinople, I suppose, across the straits, right at the entrance to the Dardanelles.

McDonald: Yes, it is in northwestern Turkey.

Hurwicz: We, of course, study events of classical Greece but that is, perhaps, four or five hundred B.C. What is the time of the Mycenaean part of the story?

McDonald: We are talking about the situation approximately one thousand years before the classical period. This little chart may give you an idea. We assign

NEAR EASTERN AND AEGEAN NEOLITHIC	*about* 8000-3000 B.C.
AEGEAN BRONZE AGE	*about* 3000-1000 B.C.
AEGEAN LATE BRONZE AGE OR MYCENAEAN AGE	*about* 1600-1100 B.C.
First Olympiad, 776 B.C.	
Homer's Lifetime, around 750 B.C.	
GREEK ARCHAIC AGE	*about* 700- 500 B.C.
GREEK CLASSICAL AGE	*about* 500- 323 B.C.
GREEK HELLENISTIC AGE	*about* 323- 146 B.C.
ROMAN PERIOD	*about* 146 B.C.-410 A.D.

about five hundred years, from 1600 to 1100 B.C. to the Mycenaean period. This is approximately the last five hundred years of the Bronze Age in that part of the world.

Hurwicz: Let me just see whether I follow this. The end of this Mycenaean period was about three thousand years ago, a little before the time of King David and Solomon. That's quite a while ago.

McDonald: Yes. Between 1200 and 1100 B.C. all these towns and many more were destroyed, burned, and there was a long period, some three hundred years, when Greece was almost completely depopulated and impoverished. We call this "the Greek Dark Ages."

Hurwicz: Do we have an explanation? Did they just suddenly get lazy, or what happened?

McDonald: There are many theories; the usual one is that a foreign enemy came in and destroyed them. There are other theories that there was an internal revolt or a terrific erosion of the arable land. Another hypothesis is that there was an epidemic or some kind of plague. In any case, after this three hundred years or so of "the Dark Ages" comes the time, we believe, that Homer himself lived, and finally the Classical Period, almost a thousand years after Mycenae flourished.

Hurwicz: Homer was talking about a period of time that was perhaps four to six hundred years before him; that is as if somebody now were writing a story about the time of the Magna Carta, or something of that sort. It took quite a good memory. Did he have any documents to rely on?

McDonald: Homer was not there, although the archeologist Heinrich Schliemann and many ancient Greeks thought he was.

15

Left: Heinrich Schliemann, son of a poor German pastor, is credited with the discovery of the Homeric World. Since childhood Schliemann was fascinated with the stories of Homer and became determined to find the towns of Homer's time. Right: Dr. Carl Blegen, professor emeritus of classical archaeology, University of Cincinnati, Ohio (1887-   ).

Hurwicz: There is one thing a person like myself tends to be a little skeptical about. How is it you really know all these ages? We do not have a well-regulated calendar or a daily newspaper where we can go back to the files for this.

McDonald: No, this is a very complicated business, particularly for a period when there was no written history. We have no written documents in Greek that can give us dates like 1600 B.C. or 1100 B.C.

Hurwicz: Naturally, they would not have known it was B.C.

McDonald: No. Even in classical times they had to use other fixed points.

Hurwicz: The original point of reference was the first Olympiad and that was about 800 B.C., wasn't it?

McDonald: It was 776, and again, they did not know it was B.C. What we have to do in this early period is to refer to nearby cultures in touch with Greece, cultures that did have written records that early.

Hurwicz: In other words, the Greeks were not the most advanced group for the time.

McDonald: No, they were a good deal behind the Egyptians, I must confess, as well as behind some of the other people of the Near East.

Hurwicz: I know it hurts you to admit it. Let's keep it a secret.

McDonald: For instance, there is a kind of pottery in Mycenaean Greece that is called Amarna pottery.

16

Hurwicz: I thought Amarna was someplace in Egypt and not in Greece.

McDonald: Yes, it is; however, in the 18th dynasty, the Egyptian king called Ikhnation, moved his capital to this new site, and built his palace. It lasted only for a generation. We know the dates from Egyptian records.

Hurwicz: He was the unsuccessful religious heretic with a good looking queen.

McDonald: We know the date when he built his new palace. It was occupied for just a quarter of a century, about 1375 to 1350 B.C. In the ruins of that palace some fragments of pottery of this sort have been found. These are vases in which the Greeks apparently sent perfumed oil over to Egypt.

Hurwicz: The theory is they could not make it after it was deposited there.

Amarna pottery.[4]

---

[4] Frank H. Stubbings, *Mycenaean Pottery from the Levant* (Cambridge University Press, 1951), plate **XVIII**.

McDonald: That's right. So we can date this particular type of Mycenaean pottery within that quarter of a century or slightly earlier. Then we have found exactly similar pottery. It is a definite phase of Mycenaean pottery.

When we find it in the mainland we can date it and everything that is in the same layer to this same date, about 1375 to 1350. In this way we establish what are called synchronisms or cross dating from a culture that has a known chronology to the Greek culture. For instance, sometimes we find Egyptian scarabs, or Mesopotamian cylinder seals, in Greece.

Hurwicz: Scarabs?

McDonald: Scarabs were made in the shape of a beetle. Some of them have inscriptions on them.

So, again, if we find a scarab in Greek layer with an inscription that proves its date, we can date the Greek layer and everything in it. By this system of synchronisms, or cross dating, we gradually establish these early dates.

Hurwicz: Just to check up on you again, the confidence in those Egyptian dates comes—I suppose—from the documented history, or from astronomy perhaps?

McDonald: Professor Wright was quizzing me about this before the program began. I would not like to be placed on the spot to say exactly how we can depend on the Egyptian dates. There are king lists that have been gradually revised and refined until they are pretty sure. For instance, the beginning of the Eighteenth Dynasty in Egypt was about 1570, and this is synchronous with the beginning of the Mycenaean period.

Hurwicz: It's amazing that we probably know more about early Greek history than about early English history in some cases. I find this very remarkable that one can establish such firm foundations in this field. I am tempted to get you to tell us a little bit about how it is that we were so ignorant about it a hundred years ago when we know so much about it now.

McDonald: The history of the excavation of prehistoric Greece is, I think, a fascinating one. It extends over about three generations, roughly. In the first generation, before 1900, there is no doubt that the great name was that of Heinrich Schliemann. Most people have heard of Schliemann, I suppose. His father was an impoverished German clergyman, who told him about the Homeric poems. Neither the father nor the son read them in Greek, but in German.

Heinrich Schliemann decided as a boy that he wanted to prove by excavation that Homer really knew what he was talking about, that he had not been imagining Troy and Agamemnon, Mycenae, and the rest. To do that he had to make a fortune, which he did by middle life.

Hurwicz: You mean he made a fortune to be able . . .

McDonald: Yes, to be able to excavate Homer's Troy. This is what he tells us in his autobiography, anyway. He went over to the area of northwest Turkey. The site of Troy was not known for sure, but most people who really believed there had been a Troy had picked a different site altogether. Schliemann chose a hill called Hissarlik and began to excavate in 1870.

Hurwicz: That was over ninety years ago.

McDonald: Yes. He immediately began to find ruins earlier—lower down—than the Greek. There had been a Roman level, then a Greek level, but below that, one before the other, several earlier levels.

Schliemann was sure that this must be the site of Homeric Troy. However, he picked the wrong level to begin with. He chose the second level from the bottom mainly because he found a lot of gold as well as impressive fortifications.

Hurwicz: Why did you say he found the wrong level? What he identified as Homer's Troy was something else perhaps?

McDonald: I am jumping ahead. He could not have known it was the wrong level. We can now date it fairly accurately and it turned out to be about a thousand years earlier than the time that the Trojan War took place. We now believe that the Troy captured by the Greeks was the seventh level from the bottom.

I should go on to tell you that Schliemann moved from Troy to the mainland at Mycenae. The walls of Mycenae had always been visible, the great fortifications that you saw in the reconstruction earlier. Schliemann began to excavate inside the walls. He discovered a circle of stone slabs, and deep down some 20 feet below them he came upon six royal graves. I suppose that was the

Mycenae death mask.

richest archaeological find, except for the tomb of King Tut-Ankh-amon, that has ever been made. In these shaft graves there were 19 people buried. He was quite sure he had found the tombs of Agamemnon and Clytemnestra.

Among other contents, he found a number of gold masks like this one which had been placed over the faces of some of the people buried in the graves.

Hurwicz: This is kind of a three-dimensional photograph of one of the persons buried.

McDonald: They seem to be real impressions taken in wax and then transferred to a wooden core and then beaten out in thin gold.

Hurwicz: It gives us something of an anthropological type.

McDonald: You can see the beard, the heavy eyebrows, the generally aristocratic type.

Hurwicz: It looks like a Greek nose.

McDonald: This has sometimes been said. Schliemann thought that this was Agamemnon's own portrait.

Then in the next generation after Schliemann's time, from 1900 to World War I, a major figure was Sir Arthur Evans. He went down to Crete and excavated there, particularly at the site of Knossos. It was the most important place in "Crete of the hundred cities."

At Knossos, Sir Arthur Evans found evidence for a highly-developed culture even earlier than the Mycenaean, perhaps going back to almost 2000 B.C. He called it the Minoan civilization.

Hurwicz: Was he referring to the legendary king, Minos?

McDonald: Yes, Minos of legend. So he called the whole culture "Minoan." He thought that the Minoans had controlled the mainland. We do not think so now, but we do think that Minoan culture had a very strong influence on the mainland of Greece, and we even talk about the Minoan-Mycenaean culture, from about 2000 to 1000 or 1100, as the first highly developed European civilization.

Hurwicz: Of course, as it was noted that Egypt was, at that time, at the higher level of culture, it would be natural for Crete to be the transmitter.

McDonald: Yes, Crete was in many respects the intermediary between the Near East and the Mycenaeans. You might be interested in a picture of a reconstruction of the very sophisticated Cretan architecture, and also the costumes of the court ladies.

Hurwicz: Well, I see that the era of the topless garment for women is not really a revolution. That was over three thousand years ago.

McDonald: You might call it sophisticated—or perhaps primitive. Well, anyway, from wall paintings, statuettes and so on, he was able to make these reconstructions.

In the third generation, since World War I, starting in the twenties, I would say the greatest excavator in our area is Carl Blegen.

An example of Cretan architecture and court ladies attending the queen.[5]

Hurwicz: He, I think, has some Minnesota connections.

McDonald: That's right. Carl Blegen was born in the Twin Cities, was educated at Augsburg College and at the University of Minnesota. His father was a professor of Greek at Augsburg College.

Hurwicz: I suppose since we are on a Graduate School program here, we should mention his brother, Theodore, who was dean of the Graduate School for a number of years.

McDonald: Yes, the Blegen family is a distinguished Minnesota family. Carl Blegen has excavated many sites in southern and central Greece, but, particularly, he carried out a re-examination of the site of Troy. It was he who showed conclusively that Schliemann's second level was much too early and that even the sixth level had been mistakenly called Homeric Troy.

Hurwicz: However, to be fair to Schliemann, he excavated before people knew how to do it in a scientific way.

---

[5] *The Epic of Man,* Editors of *Life* (New York: Time Incorporated, 1961), p. 146. Reprinted by permission. Copyright, 1961, by Time, Incorporated. Drawn by Rudolph F. Zallinger.

McDonald: Yes, he lacked knowledge and techniques now available. Well, the most recent place in which Blegen has dug is at Pylos, down in the southwest. We think it is the palace of Nestor, another important king at the time of the Trojan War.

Hurwicz: It is also a place to which you commute more or less regularly.

McDonald: I guess I have been back there about six or seven times now.

Hurwicz: I think you know more about it than Nestor did.

This matter of palaces and dresses is very interesting. Another thing I find very fascinating is the question of how writing played a role in these matters. You said that there is no documented Greek history, but it seems to me I have been reading about some very exciting decipherments from this era.

McDonald: I would say that the Mycenaean period was on the verge of history. It is in between. We generally talk about historic versus prehistoric. Historic culture is one where we have written records which can be read and used to reconstruct events. A pre-historic culture is one where there are no written records, and its study depends entirely upon archaeological evidence.

Hurwicz: Professor Wright will get to that point.

McDonald: Yes, the time span he deals with is entirely prehistoric. In between, however, there is a gray area. For instance, at Knossos, beginning in 1900, Sir Arthur Evans found documents, mostly clay tablets, written in three different scripts. The latest one, which he called Linear B, was in use just before the final destruction of the palace. He found thousands of these Linear B tablets. We have a picture of one just like them which was found at Pylos. Evans could never decipher this Linear B writing system. He did not publish very many tablets.

Hurwicz: This is a very interesting script. Is this Linear B we are looking at?

McDonald: Right. That is a Linear B tablet from Pylos. I was going to say that Evans, for forty years, kept several thousand of these tablets. He could not read them; he did not publish enough for anyone else to work on them.

Hurwicz: He was very selfish in some ways.

McDonald: He wanted to be the one to make the decipherment.

In 1939 at Pylos, we found several hundred more tablets in the very same kind of script, Linear B, as had been found in Crete. This time Professor Blegen decided that he would publish the tablets right away. The war intervened, but in 1951 they were published. Some photographs had been passed around before then. In 1952, a very brilliant young Englishman, Michael Ventris, succeeded in the decipherment of Linear B.

Hurwicz: He was not even a professional classicist. Is that fair to mention?

McDonald: Furthermore, he was not a cryptanalyst, as was often said in the press. He was an architect by profession.

Hurwicz: What did the language turn out to be?

Line drawing of a Pylos tablet showing syllabic script,
Linear B Tablet No. 20.[6]

McDonald: Evans always took it for granted that it was an unknown Minoan language, and this is one reason he found it so difficult to decipher. It turned out, however, to be Greek, a very early form of Greek, at least four-hundred years before the earliest written Greek we have, which is in the Homeric poems and in some inscriptions of about 750 B.C. These Pylos tablets, by the way, were burned in the destruction of the palace of Nestor and so were preserved. Since they were originally only sun dried, they would have completely disintegrated in time had it not been for the fire.

Hurwicz: Did you find any historical information in them?

McDonald: Unfortunately, I think you can still say that even Pylos is mainly prehistoric.

There is no political history in the wider sense in the documents. They are mostly economic texts. It is rather ironical that these earliest written records from the European continent have to do mainly with two all too common subjects: war and taxes.

I think particularly on April 14 it may be appropriate to mention taxes.[7]

---

[6] Emmett L. Bennett, Jr. (editor), *The Pylos Tablets* (Princeton University Press, 1955), p. 3. Reprinted by permission. Copyright, 1955, by Princeton University Press.

[7] This program was telecast on April 14, 1965.

Hurwicz: When I think that the main topics seem to be topless dresses, war, and taxes, I do not know how much progress has been made.

What about this tablet here that shows the symbols?

McDonald: It is a syllabic script. Each one of these symbols stands for a syllable. There are four words here. The words are separated by short vertical strokes.

It seems to say: "This is the way the ancient (or aged) wine was distributed." Below there is a list of nine towns. Over here on the right—and Evans knew this—are numbers. They had the decimal system. The circle is one hundred, the horizontal line ten, and the vertical line the digit. So this town got a hundred casks or jugs of wine. This one got thirty-five and so on.

Hurwicz: Let me come back to another point you made earlier about Schliemann's great belief in Homer's words. Was he finally vindicated, or not?

McDonald: Schliemann was partly right—and I suppose partly wrong. He was right that the Homeric poems did have history behind them. But Homer did not live in Mycenaean times and he must have gotten these stories from earlier generations of oral poets.

Hurwicz: I see a rather puzzling item here. I do not know exactly what it is. Is it also from those excavations?

McDonald: This cup is from one of the graves in the grave circle of Mycenae. In the eleventh book of the *Iliad,* Homer tells about a cup that belonged to Nestor. He had taken it to Troy with him. Homer says that: "It was a magnificent beaker, adorned with golden studs, which the old man had brought from home. It had four handles. Each was supported by two legs, and on top of each, facing one another, was a pair of golden doves." Until the time Schliemann found this cup, nobody had ever seen such a cup and people could not understand Homer's description. Then Schliemann found this cup. There, truly, was Nestor's cup.

Hurwicz: I do not think anyone could have invented such a thing.

McDonald: Here are the gold rivets and the gold birds on the rim; here are— and this was the most puzzling thing about the written description—the legs or struts that joined the handles to the base. Fortunately it has only two handles, for I do not know how one would drink out of it if it had four.

Hurwicz: Also, I suppose people might think that this was a forgery by Schliemann. I think there should be a small deviation.

McDonald: When Schliemann found this, he said: "Aha! that's Nestor's cup." Agamemnon must have gotten hold of it at Troy and brought it back with him to Mycenae and it was buried with him.

However, from the pottery found with it, we know that this cup was buried no later that 1500 B.C., and we believe that the Trojan War took place about 1250. The cup had been buried well over 250 years before the Trojan War and couldn't be the one Nestor had with him.

Hurwicz: Yet there might have been another such cup, and one of those might have been taken.

A replica of Nestor's cup which was found in the excavated Mycenae Shaft Graves at Mycenae is shown. It is nearly 6 inches tall and has doves at the top of each handle.

McDonald: There might have been, but the point I'd like to make is that there is almost surely a connection between this cup and the Homeric description. Therefore, if the type went out of use as early as 1500 B.C., it proves the tremendous length of time over which the poetic tradition developed.

Hurwicz: I think we may want to pursue some of these points a little further, but I would like to consider the setting of this whole period we have been discussing here. When we look at your chronology, 1600 B.C. sounds like a long time ago. Yet you refer to this as the late Bronze Age. Apparently this is a rather recent period in the overall human history. I think perhaps this might be the appropriate time to ask Professor Wright where he would place this period in relation to that part of prehistory he has been studying in connection with excavations in which he has participated. Professor Wright, what is the historical setting of this late Bronze Age? Do you consider it something very old, or is it rather recent by your standards?

Professor Wright: The Mycenaean Period was young in comparison to that part of prehistoric time when people began to live together in villages with agriculture and domesticated animals. This occurred in perhaps 10,000 B.C., in contrast to the 1200 B.C. of the late Bronze Age.

Hurwicz: You are not very impressed by Professor McDonald's dates. They are ancient history.

Wright: I cannot say I am not impressed. He has so much more information on which to base a reconstruction of people's activities.

Hurwicz: Well, you have to talk about villages; he has palaces to show.

Wright: There are no nice gold objects that can be shown in museums.

Hurwicz: You deal in less valuable materials. But let me ask you this. We are interested on this program in the time factor in these developments, not merely in the story, fascinating as it may be. What is the crucial time aspect of the prehistorical investigations you have been making?

Wright: I think we might look at this in the perspective of all historical time and the critical areas of prehistoric time—let us say, since the beginning of agriculture, about the last ten to twelve thousand years.

Now, the layman looks at time best from his own position of familiar people and historical documents. He has little trouble visualizing what has happened in the early years of this century, even of the last century, because the language, at least in his own country, is usually the same. The dress is very much the same, as are the customs, and so on. For the earlier periods, let's say Elizabethan time, it is certainly more difficult and even more so with Roman, Greek, Babylonian, and so on. The customs were different, as was the language. Back beyond that we have no historical record, or tablets of any kind, decipherable or not.

Hurwicz: What is the dating of the earliest written tablets that we know about?

Wright: In Mesopotamia, or modern Iraq, it is around 3500 B.C. or 3000 B.C., and in Egypt about the same time.

Hurwicz: That is quite a bit earlier than the Mycenaean age, but when you go back to the beginning of agriculture, you have to go back another six to seven thousand years.

Wright: A lot happened in that time. This brings up the point that the pace of cultural changes has greatly increased. Fifty or one hundred thousand years ago people living in the Stone Age hunted wild game, and they changed their way of life very little for hundreds or thousands of years—a very slow development.

Hurwicz: Do you not imagine that the aborigines of New Guinea or the interior of Australia, who are running around naked and spearing kangaroo, were doing pretty much the same thing perhaps two thousand years or even, perhaps, four thousand years ago. Is this the kind of static type of situation to which you are referring?

Wright: Certainly we can see such a contrast at the present time in many regions of the world, and a few hundreds of years ago the contrast was right here in this country between the Indian and the white man who settled in the sixteenth and seventeenth centuries.

Hurwicz: Do you feel that the big moment of cultural change was this switch from a primitive hunting economy to agriculture about twelve thousand years ago?

Wright: I would speak of it as a revolution, because it brought about an increase in the pace of cultural development of peoples, their association with one another, and particularly their control of the environment. This revolution, involving the domestication of plants and animals about 8000 or 10000 B.C., led progressively to the greater and greater perfection of tools and the building of larger villages to the point where they became towns. Then in due time came the development of writing and the organization of very large towns and large cities. The development of large cities in the Mesopotamian lowland really led to highly developed political and sociological organization whereby nature could be controlled. This is particularly important in Mesopotamia because the cities were located along the Tigris and Euphrates Rivers, which were really wild rivers like—let us say—the Minnesota and Mississippi Rivers.

Hurwicz: Except they did not have a U.S. Corps of Engineers.

Wright: Well, to a degree they did; that is, they had a central organization which could control the rivers. They had to in order to support the cities with irrigation agriculture.

Hurwicz: The cities you are talking about are cities like the one from which Abraham was supposed to have come. Now, let me ask you this. What sort of evidence do you have for the time of this earlier period when agriculture was introduced? I think you, yourself, have taken part in many of these expeditions like the one to Jarmo in Mesopotamia, or more recently, Turkey. What do you find there? You do not find the beautiful golden cups. What is it that gives you the information?

Wright: Actually what appears on the surface is just a low mound of dirt, but on this mound are small fragments of pottery or chipped stone. There are never any gold objects. These stone objects are clearly made by man. Our procedure then is to start digging after permission from the government has been obtained.

Hurwicz: Let us take a look at this map just so we can orient ourselves a little bit and see where we are when we talk about these very earliest villages.

Wright: In the lowland are the Tigris and Euphrates Rivers. The Mesopotamian lowland, with the Tigris and Euphrates Rivers, is between the Persian Gulf and the Mediterranean Sea. It is bounded in the North by a very conspicuous range of mountains, which actually continues eastward to the Himalayas and westward to Turkey. This high mountain range separates the plateaus of Anatolia and Persia on the north from the Mesopotamian lowland on the south. The foothills of the mountains are quite favorable for farming. In fact, this is the major region of agriculture for the present countries of Iraq, Syria, and Turkey.

Hurwicz: Now, from these investigations and excavations there, do we have any idea about what a village, a farming community, of this very early period looked like?

Wright: Certain reconstructions have been made, based upon the artifacts or the objects that have been taken out of these ancient villages, made of obsidian, a volcanic glass. It cuts to a very sharp edge. Such stone pieces were set along in a curved piece of wood. They were often sealed into the wood with asphalt, which happened to be available locally. This locality was rather close to the great oil fields of Iraq.

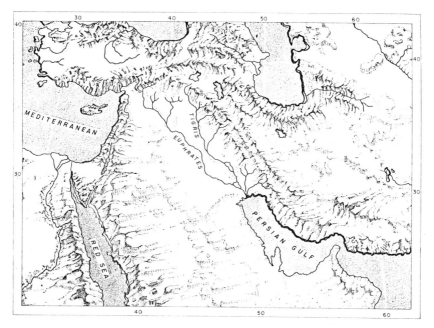

The Zagros Mountains, bounding the Mesopotamian Lowland of the Tigris and Euphrates Rivers, were one area in which agriculture and animal domestication had their beginnings. The foothills of the mountains contained natural habitats for wild grains and the wild animals, like sheep and goats, that were domesticated 7000-9000 B.C.

Hurwicz: Asphalt was available, but did they have the obsidian, too?

Wright: The obsidian is interesting. It came from a volcanic area in Turkey about 125 miles away. This is extremely important archaeologically, because it is really the first well documented trade item in that region. Ten thousand years ago, people apparently had sufficient communication with their neighbors to be able to trade this item. This brings up the whole matter of communications between people here, even at these earliest times.

Hurwicz: Do you think they developed these techniques of communication first and this led to agriculture? What accounts for that revolution of which you were speaking?

Wright: Well, there are various hypotheses about this. One of the older ones is that during the Glacial period about twelve, fifteen, or twenty thousand years ago, the ice sheet covered northern Europe and northern North America. During this period, the climate in Mesopotamia and elsewhere in the Mediterranean region was much colder and wetter than it is now, especially in the summertime. The idea is that after the glacial period, when it became dry again, all the people were crowded towards the oases. These are areas of springs or desert lakes.

Typical modern village in Northern Iraq in the foothills of the Zagros Mountains. Archaeological excavations indicate that primitive farming villages of 7000 B.C. had similar ground plans.

Hurwicz: Were these people who, at that time, had not invented agriculture?

Wright: They were hunters. They moved to these regions not only because that was where the water was, but also because the animals went there. The close proximity of the game animals and men is supposed to have led to domestication of these animals. That is one hypothesis. There is another one, and this one I personally favor. Perhaps it was not any climatic determinism that caused the development of agriculture, but just the gradual cultural development of these people: increase in population, perfection of tools, and increasing control of the environment. With greater population there came more ideas for new tools, and so on. Apparently they gradually began to experiment with plants rather than just gathering seeds. Perhaps they dropped seeds in a few places and noticed that, in the following year, crops came up which they could in turn harvest. In any case, in the foothill belt in Mesopotamia there is a great geographic diversity, with different kinds of soil and different kinds of vegetation. Even if there were some climatic changes of importance, the critical ecological zones could simply move up and down the mountains and the people could follow them.

Hurwicz: Are you saying that you do not think that climate was a very important factor? You seem to be questioning some of the ideas that prevail or have prevailed.

Wright: I would say there is good evidence that climate did change at the end of the Glacial period, but I feel it still has to be proven that this has much to do with the cultural evolution itself and the development of agriculture.

Hurwicz: I'd like to go back to the excavations at Jarmo or thereabouts. I wonder if we could actually take a look at the way these things are found in the ground. What is the specific evidence for wheat, for example? How do you find out about that?

Wright: The excavation of one of these sites begins at the surface and proceeds downward. This picture shows the trench to a depth of about three feet from the uppermost soil surface. The men are picking away at the ground and putting on

Workmen uncovering stone foundations of houses of an early farming village of about 7000 B.C. at Jarmo in the foothills of Iraq.

the mats such objects as pottery, stone, and so on. They uncovered rows of stones which turned out to be the foundations for small houses very much like the modern houses in the nearby villages.

Hurwicz: Would you say people live now the way they did ten thousand years ago?

Wright: The modern people in this area are getting modern objects; a status symbol these days is a transistor radio. Five years ago when I was there it was something else. However, the basic agricultural methods are still the same. In these excavations sometimes little concentrations of charred wheat and barley grains come out. These can be identified, specifically, as cultivated types rather than the wild wheat and barley. The same is true of the bones of domesticated animals.

Hurwicz: Can you get some idea of the chronology? Are there strata there?

Wright: There are very distinct layers. Actually the absolute chronology, when I speak of ten thousand to twelve thousand years ago, is based upon the technique of radio-carbon dating, which is accurate within a few hundred years.

Hurwicz: For this purpose it is good enough.

Wright: In the case of the Mycenaean period there is competition for accuracy between this method and the Egyptian king list, or some comparable historical method.

Hurwicz: Well, I think this gives us a fairly good idea of what the progress of time has meant during the last twelve thousand years of human history. I think it might be well for us to try to look into some of the questions that naturally occur to a person following these developments. Let us now join our guests, who possibly want to bring up some of the issues that we have already considered or perhaps some we have not even talked about. I think we still have unsettled scores that might take us back to the Mycenaean age. Are there any questions that have come up?

Miss Borchert: I would like to ask one question of Professor McDonald. What is the connection between the Mycenaean Age and classical Greek culture?

McDonald: That is rather a large question. There is still a lot of dispute over it, though more in the past than recently. In general, I think it has been quite certainly proved that there were many cultural traits that survived from the Mycenaean to the Classical, even though there are a thousand years between. For instance, the ground plan of the Greek temple is almost identical to the plan of the King's megaron in the Mycenaean period.

Hurwicz: Megaron? That is Homer's name for the main part of the palace.

McDonald: Then we have the Doric order, one of the major forms of classical architecture. This also is very much like the Mycenaean and the Minoan kind of column. Athletic contests came over also, apparently, and a good deal of religious material. For instance in those Linear B tablets we find some of the names of the classical Greek gods. The epic itself is another connecting link from the Mycenaean period to the Classical.

Hurwicz: Evidently they had not completely forgotten what happened earlier. I suppose the transmission of architecture is not accidental, for architecture was the most durable thing; there were probably some things left standing they could imitate.

McDonald: Apparently so. For instance, at Knossos, high up in the fill and possibly above the surface of the Classical period, Evans found a charging bull in plaster relief. He had a theory that this was the origin of the story of the Minotaur, the bull of Minos.

Hurwicz: This is the bull to whom young people were periodically sacrificed?

McDonald: That is right. Evans found some fresco paintings, showing boys and girls turning somersaults on the back of a charging bull. Apparently the bulls were trained to put their heads down; the acrobats grabbed the horns; the bull tossed its head, and the acrobats turned somersaults.

Hurwicz: One has a feeling that these Cretans were people who appreciated entertainment of various kinds.

Mrs. Fenton: May I ask you a question? This is rather an operational kind of question, I suppose. Schliemann had a lead—if you will—in the work of Homer. How do you know where to look? How do you know, for instance, that the most advanced civilization of its time has never even been uncovered? Where does an archaeologist begin?

Wright: One way is to do surface exploration, roaming the countryside and picking up objects from the surface, asking villagers about strange objects that they cannot explain. This would certainly be one way of finding ancient sites. Certainly, there are vast areas of the eastern Mediterranean which have not been explored at all in this way.

Hurwicz: Is it not true, also, that in Palestine archaeologists sometimes follow a fairly detailed description in the Bible? A famous case, I think, was the discovery of the secret passage of Jerusalem, which was exactly as it was supposed to be, and had just been covered up some three thousand years.

McDonald: Nelson Glueck is a great believer in using the Bible as a kind of guide. I do not know whether or not it works in Greece in the case of Homer. I think in restrospect that now that we have found Nestor's palace, we have reason to believe that Homer inherited some knowledge about it through the tradition. However, I do not think you would ever have found it simply by following hints in Homer.

We use all these methods that Professor Wright mentioned. We look for a good water supply, and particularly for pottery on the surface. Usually, if you take a half hour on a hilltop and pick up a bagful of pottery, you can estimate the major phases in its history and at what periods it has been inhabited.

Wright: With the possibility of something underneath.

McDonald: You cannot be sure that you have gotten the whole story until you excavate, but you often have a pretty good idea ahead of time.

Wright: Jericho is a good example of this, because of course there were stories of the walls of Jericho. Yet it was only recently that excavation went to the very bottom of this extremely early village site, which dates from something like 8000 B.C., at the very bottom. It was located there because of the tremendous water supply from the springs.

Borchert: These things you have mentioned stem from works of literature. Homer's *Iliad* and *Odyssey,* the *Bible,* even the tales of the battles of Jericho. How do you go back when you were talking about before they wrote, before there were legends?

Wright: This is really more a matter of the kind of surface exploration that I was speaking of without any historical written guides. The only guide one might have for a particular region is the fact that if people lived there in historic time it is likely they lived there before, because it was good land with a good water supply. Particularly for the agricultural periods, it was good land. However, for the prehistoric periods, for the hunting cultures, the Stone Age, it would not be very reasonable to look there; it is better to look in the mountains where there are caves and animals.

Time and Sociological Change

In striving to identify "laws" of social life, sociologists become involved in concepts of time.

SPEAKER: *ROY G. FRANCIS*, PROFESSOR OF SOCIOLOGY

COMMENTATORS: *DOUGLAS M. HEAD*, MINNEAPOLIS ATTORNEY AND FORMER STATE LEGISLATOR

                            DONAL M. MORRISON, MINNEAPOLIS *Star* COLUMNIST

Professor Francis: Sociology is involved in time in two major—and perhaps confusing—ways. On one hand it takes time for social action to take place. If we are studying marital adjustment or the consequences of a social organization, it takes time for this behavior to occur. On the other hand, the data that we look at are also wrapped up in history. The forces that are operating at the moment of time in which we are doing our studying might be changing the whole network of forces that result in human behavior. Although our primary interest is in identifying social process, the process itself is caught up in history. This is essentially what I want to point out this evening and to illustrate in three or four different ways.

Although time, as most people think of it, is unidirectional, probably not retrievable, we have to look at time as containing a series of dimensions or different aspects. I will borrow something from an historian, Frederick Teggart. He argued that we have to observe the social things that persist over a period of time, the things that are changing slowly over time, and those things that are so hurriedly changing that they appear to us and to the people in the situation as an event.

I would like to call your attention to a rather simple piece of information here. On this graph—which is really a double graph—the broken line reflects the number of live births per year in the United States and the metric is in "millions." We see that in the beginning of this century there were something less than three million live births per year. The total number was irregularly increasing and then it began to decrease. Somewhere around 1938-39, the number began to increase again. Sometimes we can see a slow pattern of change; but other times we can observe something that is so dramatic that we call it an event.

I think we can see some events take place here, where there is suddenly a dramatic change. It does not take much for an historian to say, "This point where the number of births decreases is just about the time we got involved in World War II." Later we see dramatic increment of change occurring again at a moment of time and then we say ,"Obviously, this is when the GI's came back."

However, most social changes are not so easily apparent. What happens is this: either in terms of absolute numbers or in terms of a rate of change, a decline can occur over a long period of time. Change can occur and society will not feel it until a few years have passed. I want to illustrate that point beginning in the depression years where we reach the bottom of the birth rate and the lowest number of births. Notice that the number of births during the depression is ac-

The Family Through TIME

Rock-a-bye Baby School days, school days! **BEATLES: IT'S BEEN A HARD DAY'S NIGHT** MINNESOTA HATS OFF TO THEE!

Wedding March *Rock-a-bye Baby* *Wedding March* again *Rock-a-bye Baby*

Announcer: "And here we are again, ladies and gentlemen, at the auditorium for the wrestling match of the century. . ."

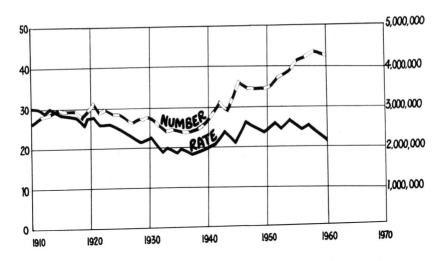

LIVE BIRTHS & BIRTH RATES: United States·1909-1960

tually less than it was in 1920 or even 1910. Both the absolute number and the birth rate are less, even though the population has increased. The number of births at this historic point will affect the schools, of course, five years later, high schools twelve or thirteen years later, colleges even later, and the labor market still later. The kids who were born in 1935 entered the labor force around 1955 at a time when the birth rate had increased enormously. Although births had increased by 1955, the number of people who were ready to enter the labor force, ready to take jobs, was relatively small. As a matter of fact, it turns out that the number of people ready to join the labor force at the time of the Korean War was about 30 per cent less than it was in 1920, even though the fifties was a time when our economy was expanding very rapidly. I think we have to observe that there is a certain kind of lag that we are talking about.

When the post-war baby boom occurred right at this point (1946), there were all sorts of predictions about how our farm surplus was going to be eaten up. Of course, a child will eat a little jar of baby food and not a half-dozen hamburgers as a teenager would. Before we would have an appreciable dent in our farm production, we would have to wait awhile. In the meantime, agricultural production improved. There was no appreciable gain in consumption.

It is intriguing to observe that the people who were born in the 30's were the women who were becoming mothers at the time of the Korean War. Although the rate was apparently going down, a small number of women were having, relatively, a large number of children. One reason the rate behaved that way is just due to the arithmetic. The birth rate is found by dividing the number of births by the total population. If you keep adding between three and four million births a year, for five to ten years, you are going to inflate the bottom part of the fraction without appreciably changing the numerator. The rate will tend to go down from that alone.

The people who were born in 1935 are now about 30 years of age. In about five more years they will enter the age bracket in which we expect to find people becoming junior executives and receiving other promotions because of rewards in our system. Remember, this group consists of a small number of people. There will not be as many of them (in the 35 to 40-year age bracket) in 1970 as there were in any of the previous 20 to 30 years.

Mr. Head: Is this a factor already affecting corporations, business plans, and policies?

Francis: Yes, the question has occurred to personnel managers. Where can they get talent when we have such a small number? Well, they can get women and give them managerial positions. Some industries and activities are doing this. They can promote people who were once passed over. For instance, a company may promote a man to foreman whom it felt was inadequate. I understand that in some of the mining companies along the iron range, as well as elsewhere, they had to promote some people who previously would not have been promoted. A company cannot invest time to train anyone else for this kind of work.

Mr. Morrison: Are you saying it is time for me to ask for a raise?

Francis: This will last for about ten years. You see what will happen. They might then begin to promote younger people. If the decision is to promote younger people instead of those between 35 and 40, promotions will be given between ages 30 and 35. However, the post-war baby boom started around 1945. Five years after this decision, say, in 1975, these kids will be reaching age 30, and will be demanding promotions. There are an enormous number of them compared with those today—almost a million more a year. Probably there will not be enough positions to go around at that time.

Professor Hoyt: Do you suppose automation may change this picture and may be a factor disturbing the extrapolation?

Francis: I think automation will almost destroy the statement made so far. Also, automation will require a different kind of training. The people who are being trained in the areas of mathematics for handling the automation process will be in a good position. Those who are not trained will find that their jobs—even if they are managers—could be automated out of existence. One of the decisions which businesses face is whether or not to automate management.

Morrison: Does this example then show how sociology must go with the time-lag problem?

Francis: Yes, I think what it says is that if we are to profitably interpret the critical data, we must put the raw information about people's behavior into a historical context. The same point can be shown a little more dramatically here, where we make another little point. These rates are the birth order. The first one is the birth rate for the first child, the second for the second child, and so on up to the seventh child. Actually, we could plot up to the seventeenth child, but you would not see anything on this chart.

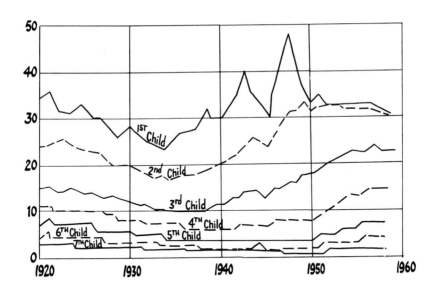

BIRTH RATES ADJUSTED FOR UNDERREGISTRATION·U.S. 1920-59 BY LIVE BIRTH ORDER, FOR NATIVE WOMEN · *Rates per 1000 ages 15·44*

Head: What do you mean by the birth rate of the first child?

Francis: We start by taking the number of women who could have children. We think of that group of women as aged 15 to about 45, because they account for ninety-nine per cent of the births—with a few rare exceptions, I would think. When we take the number of first children born to the women, and divide by the total number of women, we get the rate for the first child. Then we take the number of second children born to the women and divide it by that same denominator to get the rate for the second child, and so on.

Head: It has no relation to age of the women?

Francis: Age is important only in that we stay within that bracket, that is, 15 to 45. Notice that the rate of the first child responds to all the immediacies of history. Here, more clearly than the other chart—you can tell when the war began, when the depression was, and when people decided that maybe having a child would either provide a namesake in case they got killed in the war or would get them out of military service. You can do a lot of dating just by that.

Morrison: Could I ask a question here? Do these cycles go by generations? My parents and yours too, were from large families. I mean three to six children or more. My parents had three children, but most of their friends had only one child.

Our generation came along with many children. Is this pure history, or is it possible that the child is reacting to the fact that he or she was an only child and is not going to act in the same way?

Francis: I think there are also other things involved. The period from 1920 to 1930 was characterized by a big push for Americanization in our society. The American Legion and others found that there were millions of unnaturalized aliens who intended to stay here, and there were many forces to make the people become Americanized. One way of proving you were not an immigrant would be to have a small family. At that time the recent immigrants typically had large families, and "native whites" had smaller ones.

Morrison: Something like this really had an effect on family size? It sounds incredible but somehow sensible.

Francis: What is striking to me about this graph is that the more children the woman has, the less influence the immediacies have.

Head: Do you mean the external factors?

Francis: That's right. The external factors seem to be less significant. You can find long-term historical patterns.

Head: History seems to take longer to effect the decisions whether or not to have another child.

Francis: The decision to change from 'husband and wife' to 'father and mother' is rather a dramatic decision. Here the couple takes into account many things. Having made the decision, then the day-by-day variation of history seems to be less significant. If a couple is committed to a large family, immediate local history does not make a difference then.

Head: How much effect did the war have on the birth rate?

Francis: The rate did not go down as dramatically during the war years as during the depression.

Morrison: Wait a minute? You are saying it is a momentous decision which a couple makes—to have their first child?

Francis: I do not want to say that this is true for all couples, but I will argue it. There is a striking difference between the birth pattern at earlier periods of time and the birth pattern now. The earlier birth pattern had almost twice as many— in some areas in the United States, three times as many childless couples as could be explained on purely biological grounds. There must have been two or three times as many couples wilfully not having children during this earlier period of history. Now the childless couples are just about the number not having the capacity to have children. So that sort of change has occurred.

Holt: Has the growing practice of adoption been taken into account?

Francis: This chart is in terms of live births, not the number of children at home. It is strictly live births.

Morrison: Where would your line go for childless couples?

Francis: There would be no way to put that in this chart. The childless couple, I think, would be more effectively shown on a different chart. Roughly about five per cent of couples cannot have children because of biological incapacity of either one or the other or both spouses. It should be a straight line on a graph.

Morrison: Where do the voluntaries go?

Francis: In some places as many as 20 per cent of the families are childless after ten or fifteen years of marriage, so they would appear as variations from the straight line implied by biological deficiency.

Head: Is this an economic matter?

Francis: I think it is economic and historical. I think it comes back to an earlier point. It seems that to be a parent involves a change in relationship. One is no longer going to be just husband or wife; one will be 'father' or 'mother.'

Morrison: Of course, it is not always voluntary.

Francis: There is some evidence that modern families are so put together that they can put up with a mistake; they may have a plan for three children and if a fourth comes along, they can afford this.

Changing Family Cycle 1890·1950

Here, I think we find a critical point made in the problem of sociological research. What we show here is essentially what we were showing at the opening of the program, the family cycle.

First, I want to point out the difference between the "gay nineties" period and the 1950 period. The first block of time, 24.1, indicates the average age at first marriage. Notice this 24.1: on the average they were marrying about 24. The next period of time is how long it took them, on the average, to get started having their children, and it is about nine months.

The next unit of time shows long it takes a family to complete having their children. This is nine years. Next there is a period of the child training, and these can overlap, obviously. After the child-training period we find the child-launching period, signified by this picture of a person leaving home. When you compare 1890 to 1950, there are some other surprising changes. First of all, the age of first marriage drops down. Secondly, it takes a little longer before they typically begin having children. Nevertheless, husbands and wives are younger by the time they begin having children than was the previous generation. They complete their families much more quickly; it took nine years in 1890 and now it takes a little less than four years. That takes into account the decline of the average size of family. The child-training period may now extend partly into college. The period when the children were leaving home was very much the same length as the child-begetting period.

Now there is something new. In 1890, before the last child left home, one or the other parent—and usually the male—would have died. There was then a period of widowhood of about 11.5 years. By 1950 a new part of the family cycle became apparent, *the husband and wife were together* when all the children had left home for marriage or career. For 13.7 years, the parents were back together as husband and wife before one or the other died, on the average. Again, typically, it was the male who died first so that the woman had something like 7.7 years as a widow.

Now the difference of age at marriage between male and female partly accounts for widowhood. But the dramatic thing, something that we do not find in the earlier cycle, is increased longevity, plus the lower marriage age and the smaller sized family, so that they were through with parenthood earlier.

Now people often complete their families by the time they are less than thirty. Their children, if they duplicate their parents, they will be having children before the parent generation is biologically worn out. I think this is making the real difference.

We need to study this and other aspects of the social process. For example, how much time does it now take to complete various aspects of the family cycle. Though families can predict certain kinds of crises, more research could be done on predicting and handling of family crises.

An example of a potential family crisis for which parents can prepare may grow out of the child-training period. We make a lot of jokes about the first day of school and how the mother has to take the child there. I think one reason for fear being experienced at this time is that the parent is on public display. The child can throw a temper tantrum and as long as it is behind the walls of the home, the public does not know what kind of a mess the parents are making out of their responsibility. When the child goes to school, parents' mistakes are highlighted. It is no wonder that parents are somewhat concerned.

The parents face other crises along the way. When the child starts serious dating, the parent is again put on the display block in a way he was not before.

Head: The parent is a much younger parent.

Francis: Yes, that's one of the changes.

Morrison: In what way is the dating different? I mean, in the 1890's people went together and got married.

Francis: I am not sure that is particularly different, because you can argue—and I think properly—that in both situations there are predictable crises. The question is: how well are our families prepared for that, though they can sit back and predict what is going to happen?

Morrison: Sanctions have changed.

Francis: I am thinking more in terms of the complexities of modern life. The question is whether the parent is trained to take the responsibilities of parenthood. In the 1890's—males in particular—would "sow their wild oats" and this was kind of expected of them. Today, there is this big pattern: One must get married; everyone's expected to get married. Pity the poor bachelor. I am sure you have all had this experience. You come home and you happen to say to your wife: "There is a new guy in the office." The wife asks "Is he married?"

Morrison: You can pity him.

Francis: The pity comes in when, suddenly, a couple of weeks later your wife says, "Don't you think it would be nice to have that nice Mr. Brown for dinner?" You have to say yes. You go along with it.

When he shows up, someone else is going to show up too—a dinner partner—because a wife just cannot rest at ease knowing that there is a single man somewhere.

I think that this is doing something to our society. We are putting great pressure on people to get married. They are responding. They are getting married earlier whether they are emotionally ready for the responsibilities or not, so much so that people are getting worried and we are introducing sex education in the high schools.

Head: Is this an economic thing? Youngsters earn enough to support themselves earlier than they could back then?

Francis: I think it is just the converse of that. I would like to go back to this first chart just for a minute to remind us of what is happening. Some of these people who were born right after World War II, that whole Mickey Mouse Club group are now entering the marriage market. In a few years, if automation continues, if our economy does not expand rapidly enough to take them into account and with the age of first marriage going down as it has been, your question becomes vital. The old folks may have to subsidize the next generation's marriage for some time, because the younger people, who have been told that they should marry young and that everyone should be married, may find that they cannot get jobs. What is going to happen? I think you have put your finger on something.

Morrison: Well, I am speaking right now of a kid who can only go out and work in a car wash but yet who probably can make about eighty dollars a week, enough at least to help rent an apartment and buy groceries. I am sure this was not true in the 1890's. The jobs existed but the money was not there.

Francis: Undoubtedly, that is part of it. It would have been true particularly in the period from around 1945 to very close to 1960. That was a period of such rapid economical expansion that anyone, virtually anyone, could get a job if he were willing. Many youngsters were able to emancipate themselves.

Head: You have drawn generalizations about the family in 1890 and then the family in 1950. Of course the family was moving from one period or stage into another as shown; but is it not true that there will be a family different from both the family of 1950 and the family of 1960 by the time we are maybe 70 or 80? Actually, the historical process always is affecting any sociological law that you try to make.

Francis: You see, our data do not come with little tags saying: this part of me is history, this part of me is process. You never know for sure. You cannot say. At least we have arrived at a pure type of family. We should learn enough now to recognize the kinds of changes that might be going on, which is the very point we have been talking about here. It might turn out that in the next generation, say 1970, when children are getting towards marriageable age, society will expect the parents to subsidize the first couple of years, if the children are married and going to college.

Head: Do you think that period in which the husband and wife are alive to-gether after the children have left home will be a time of inner stress and strain on marital relationship, or will it be one of greater ease to travel and do things that they always wanted to do such as getting education and so on? What is the impact going to be on the economy?

Francis: It depends on a number of factors. If the dourful predictions about the younger people's inability to find jobs materializes, then, of course, the parents will not be able to travel. In so far as the younger generation attempts to estab-lish itself as the family leader, then there will be tensions. It is possible that older people will have to rediscover themselves and engage in new ventures where they can locate new and meaningful relationships and identities or society will be in real trouble. We know the divorce rate goes up a little bit even now after youngsters leave home.

Head: Would you think that there will be an impact on educational institutions because of people wanting to get some additional education to have some new challenges during that period?

Francis: In so far as higher education institutions accept the notion that one does not have to be pursuing a degree in order to attend, I think there will be a great impact. That might be the implication.

I would like to call your attention to a little piece of data on this chart about the probability of voting. The point is to call attention to history. You know, in every survey we always ask one's age and sex.

Morrison: How accurate do you think the answers to the questions about age are?

Francis: There is very good reason to suspect some answers, depending upon the problem. In some cases answers are probably inaccurate. There are certainly preferred ages. Twenty-one is a nice age. Sixty-five has become a fashionable age. I imagine with the decrease in the age when you can retire on social security, there will be change in preferred ages.

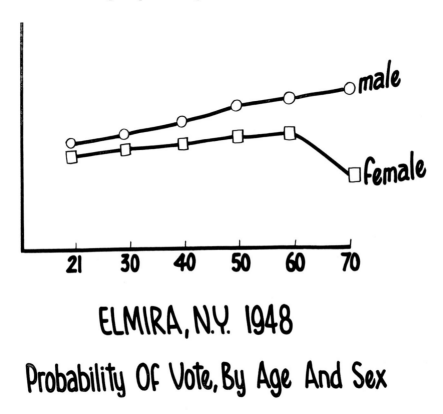

ELMIRA, N.Y. 1948

Probability Of Vote, By Age And Sex

We should ask: why do we ask the question how old one is? It has something to do with time. We assume there is some social process. There is very good reason to suspect, at least in certain areas, that the likelihood that a person will vote depends on his age. The older the person is the more he will be involved in property, the more things he will have to make him worried enough to vote. Therefore, we predicted that the probability of voting will increase with age. Sure enough, it did. There are data for 1948, that wild election. In that election, there is a steady increase in voting as age increases, especially for males, including some who were well into retirement. For females, there was also an increase according to age, but it was not as dramatic as for males. The big difference was not merely in the rate of increase. For those who were in the past sixty age-group, probability of voting went way down. The dramatic thing to me was that these people were maturing before woman suffrage was allowed.

Hoyt: Is there any correlation between the decrease in voting as shown on the chart for after age 60 and the probability that the female numbers represent widows increasingly? According to some views, the wife will vote as the husband votes. If their husbands had died, they would be less likely to vote.

Francis: Even by 1948, if a male had survived to age 21, there was a high probability that he was going to survive to between 65 and 70, so your point is partly true. It is not as true as it might have been in an earlier point in history; but it is still present, and there is no way to extract it.

Head: This same study was done again later, about 1960, wasn't it? What was the female vote?

Francis: I am not acquainted with those data. I could not say what my guess would be, since those women now would be very clearly in the widowhood category. If you did take out the non-married women and the widower, the female votes would behave much more similarly to the male votes.

Morrison: What about the woman who now is between 60 and 70?

Head: They would have been voting since 1919, which is a long time ago.

Hoyt: Could you tell us why the figures you present are from the good town of Elmira, New York? Was this selected on purpose or did it just happen?

Francis: It happened when I was writing my dissertation. This was in 1950. That moment in educational history was before foundations were putting out a great deal of money to support researchers. One looked around for data wherever they were. When the Elmira data were made available to me I took them. It's as simple as that.

Hoyt: I wonder if your data would change if you moved from Elmira to a big city, or from Elmira to a truly rural community?

Francis: I would have to guess that they would. It would depend on several factors. If you moved into a big city, probably one ethnic group would be in your sample and that could change the outcome. If you were in a big city with an ethnic group which had not become naturalized or was quite indifferent to the naturalization process, you would have another clear pattern of voting. You have to take factors like that into account.

Head: Here's another problem. Even at age 30, the male and female are very close on the Elmira voting graph. At age 50 they start to move apart. I wonder what the reason is. Is it an historical reason, or is it a process? Really, that chart cannot tell us too much until we contact Elmira in 1960, I suppose.

Francis: That's right. This is the reason why social scientists always say that further research is necessary. The first conclusion we ever announce is that more research is necessary. I think it is clear what happens. If you make a statement that is fairly clear, all it does is tell you that there are other questions that you had better answer if you are going to make sense.

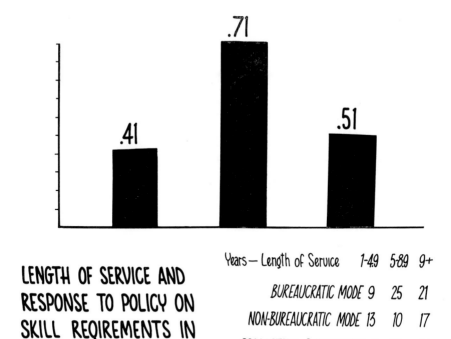

LENGTH OF SERVICE AND RESPONSE TO POLICY ON SKILL REQIREMENTS IN THE BUREAUCRACY.

Years — Length of Service	1-4.9	5-8.9	9+
BUREAUCRATIC MODE	9	25	21
NON-BUREAUCRATIC MODE	13	10	17
PROPORTION BUREAUCRATIC	.41	.71	.51

There is another way in which we can illustrate this point. This comes from a study I did in a government employment office in the city of New Orleans some years ago. Sociologists believe that if you live in a social organization any length of time, you tend to become like that organization. This is their general argument: Americans become Americans because of their society; Russians become Russians because they live in their kind of society. There are other factors, of course, but generally we argue in those terms. There is a tendency to conclude that this is true in all sorts of situations, particularly of large-scale organizations or bureaucracies.

Head: Could you define bureaucracy?

Francis: My response to "bureaucracy" is generally a negative one because bureaucrats are forever requiring me to fill out forms. By bureaucracy I simply mean a large-scale organization that involves a relatively large number of people. There is clear-cut division of labor. People specialize so that one person has this responsibility and another person has that responsibility. Not only is this systematizing done, but it is programmed into positions in the organization. The different positions are written down and people are required to behave in this way, or that way, or in another way.

Hoyt: Are these functions reduced to routine?

Francis: They are made routine as much as possible. There is a single line of authority. The line of authority is from the top down. I think it is important to understand, or to be tuned in to that notion—that it is from top down. It is really not a two-way process.

Morrison: You have just described my World War II experience.

Francis: There are bureaucratic aspects of the army. Part of our problem in service was to figure out ways to create personal relations to make the whole thing bearable. If you remember, also, the army had formal ways to get around the system itself. One of the things they had was this business of the "Verbal Orders of a Commanding Officer." If they ever wanted to legitimize something that was done in the past, they just say: "according to verbal orders of a commanding officer of a past date."

The bureaucracy always keeps records, and, of course, we kept records and records and records. Napoleon was wrong. The army does not travel on its stomach; it travels on records.

Hoyt: We had a wonderful experience of the point you are now making. One of my duties was to write the history of army ground force replacement training. To do this we went to the headquarters of the command in charge of replacement training. We were overwhelmed with archives: documents in duplicate, triplicate. We had a hard time plowing our way through. The documents would again and again lead us toward, but not quite to a conclusion. Finally, I asked permission of the commanding general to see his personal correspondence. There were all of our answers. Answers that were only hinted at by the bureaucracy and its record-keeping were spelled out in graphic language.

Head: Would part of the ultimate definition of "bureaucracy" be that the echelons below the top do not share the responsibility for the proceedings?

Francis: In a way, that would be one of the items on this graph. The top people have the responsibility for the whole show. How can they prove that the work is going on? Beyond them—somewhere—the work is being done. The obvious answer is to fill out the form. The form takes the place of the activity. At one level in a bureaucracy, people are form fillers. This is precisely what bothers us because we know that the fact that a form has been filled out does not really mean anything.

During my heroic days, when we were getting ready for our overseas duty, I was a chief clerk in an air force squadron. We had an inspection. Instead of saying that the training program was deficient because we had not done certain things, they said that the records were deficient. There is one way to make records non-deficient. Any time we had something scheduled, we would just go through the morning report of people known to be absent. Someone took toll because regulation said you had to, but we never checked roll. We just entered the stuff on the records. We went overseas with a superior calling. You would be shocked.

Hoyt: This illustrates how inaccurate official documents may be.

Francis: The point is that in a bureaucracy the forms do replace activities as far as some judgments are concerned. If the sociological argument is correct, then a person who works in a bureaucracy will take on the attitudes which make it possible for him to be a bureaucrat. In that case you ought to have people fill out forms properly.

Let me return to our study of the government employment office in New Orleans. In this office we had a number of forms to analyze. On one the clerks were describing jobs that an employer wanted to fill. I remember one of them. They were to describe the physical activities and skills necessary for a lab assistant. The clerk wrote down: "He must be able to stand up, sit down, walk around, and finger small objects." A number of the clerks would write the single word "healthy" which was not a very bureaucratic way of doing business.

We wanted to find out to what extent people who were organized into the bureaucracy accepted bureaucratic attitudes. We worked out a test. We thought you obviously could not become a bureaucrat as soon as you began employment there. It would take some time. We thought that the longer a person was on the job, the more likely he would be to give an approving response to a bureaucratic way of doing things. Preferring to make a decision personally, would be a non-bureaucratic attitude. Thinking that one ought to have a rule that tells him what to do would be a bureaucratic notion. Should we keep files, or shall we throw away files? If you say keep files, you show a bureaucratic attitude.

We classified the people as accurately as we could by whether they were committing themselves to a bureaucratic mood or not. In a graph on bureaucratic attitudes, we have the percentage of people who could be classified as accepting the bureaucratic way of doing business, plotted by how long they were employed in that agency. Some people were employed between one and five years. Other people were employed there between five and nine years. This final group of people were employed there nine years or more. Of the people who were there just a short time, 41 per cent accepted the bureaucratic way of doing business. In the next group, 71 per cent accepted it. Now if the theory is really right, the percentage will zoom up for the last group. If the man has been here a long time, he should really be a bureaucrat. However, what happens is that the per cent taking the bureaucratic view drops to 51 per cent. This study was done about 12 years ago during World War II. The people who had been there nine years or longer in this government employment office were hired during the depression years. Therefore, political-economic forces were different from when we were doing this study. Two explanations which are both plausible and somewhat related are possible.

In a government office there tends to be a relationship between how long you have been in the office and the number of promotions. It is not perfect, but there is a high correlation. It is possible that some of these people may have gone as far as they could. As soon as they felt satisfied, they could afford to thumb their noses; whereas, as long as there was something in it, one might as well act like a bureaucrat. That is a probable explanation. Also, I think, these people who are employed in an early period of time might be different from those employed later.

Tulane University and Louisiana State University have programs in both sociology and political science. Many graduates go into government service. We are training people to be bureaucrats. It is quite likely that there is a different selection in the process now than formerly. The people who were chosen to enter government service in the 1950's went there knowing that they were entering a bureaucratic sort of thing. Here we are caught up in history again. It raises the question whether or not people get to be like the system. To some extent this is true. However, it is not as overwhelmingly true as our theory would like us to believe.

Hoyt: I just wonder if there is not another explanation which perhaps fits into one of your two. I mean that at some point a person feels he has been with the organization a long time, that he has mastered the organization, that he has a leadership role in the organization. He can chart new courses with the organization. I just wonder if this would be shown in a large corporation, for example a bureaucracy, that some of the people who have been there the longest would feel the freest to strike out.

Francis: You are right. Those who were least bureaucratic were those who in their jobs were in contact with the public. We named our research monograph "Research and Procedures in a Bureaucracy," because we found that the factor which gave us the greatest departure from the bureaucratic mode, irrespective of how long the person had been there, was, to a large extent, the degree of contact with the public. If one were in contact with the public, one developed a commitment to service, and the bureaucratic mode would be disregarded.

Head: One of the things that occurs to me is that an organization, to maintain its strength, must develop ways of adapting itself to meet changing times. An organization that is going to remain viable and strong must have ways within itself to do this, and to encourage adaptation. This might not only apply to a government office, but also to a corporation.

Francis: I think there is good evidence, not so much from this study, but from other bits of sociological research, that there is a certain kind of structural deviancy that is required if an organization is to respond to changing situations. If you can have a fixed attitude on the part of management (that is, the top management), and then if they simply recruit junior people from those who reflect this attitude, you can get an organization that limits itself to one manner of performance.

Hoyt: I hate to interrupt at this point. The conversation is very interesting, but on this program "Man vs. Time," we, ourselves, are a good example of the defeat of man by time. Our time is running out. Would you take just a minute to sum up some of the salient points that have emerged from this discussion?

Francis: We can end just about where we began by saying that time is needed for the social process to work itself out. Time is involved in so many different things. Our institutions themselves have careers. The social process itself has a career. When we are trying to sort out a process in time, we must always be aware of the context in which it occurs. This makes our research extremely difficult since our sampling is often predicated on the notion that changes have not occurred. Unless we are aware of what history is going to involve us in, different rates of change as well as some things that will persist, we are not going to understand the social process. Above all, we won't be able to understand social change. Instead, we may tend to conclude that personal change is social change, which is not necessarily true.

Tick Tock Troubles

How do fundamental concepts of time become involved with concepts of space and mass?

SPEAKER: *GEORGE D. FREIER*, PROFESSOR OF PHYSICS

COMMENTATORS: *MRS. PATRICIA COLLINS*, WIFE OF THE CHAIRMAN OF THE ELECTRICAL ENGINEERING DEPARTMENT
WALTER TRENERRY, ST. PAUL ATTORNEY AND PRESIDENT OF THE MC KNIGHT FOUNDATION

Professor Hurwicz: Although we have been looking at the role of time in its human and social aspects, the concept and measurement of time are largely in the domain of physics and mechanics. Most of us, when we try to define the concept of time, find it a pretty slippery job. How is it, Professor Freier, that you as a physicist manage to avoid some of these difficulties?

Professor Freier: I would like to point out that time, as one of our fundamental concepts, cannot be easily isolated from other fundamental concepts of physics. In physics there are three fundamental concepts: mass, length, and time. Here we will be primarily interested in time.

A material particle cannot occupy two points at the same time, so what we actually do is invent time to carry us through space. As a result of this we end up with motion. Time is a consequence of motion. I would like to point out first that most of our measurements of time involve measurements in space. We are then really concerned with motions. For instance, if we observe a movie of a rocket launching, we can observe the motion of the rockets. Suddenly let us stop the motion by stopping the film and ask: Why do you think the rocket stopped?

Hurwicz: I would not dare to guess. Perhaps one of our visitors can conjecture.

Mr. Trenerry: It has to do with time.

Freier: Yes, but more importantly we were visualizing the *motion* of the rocket. The reason that we say that the rocket stopped is that there was some other motion persisting. If *all* material particles stopped at the same instant that the rocket stopped, we would have no way of knowing that the rocket had stopped. It is incorrect to think of time as some invisible flowing fluid which simply moves onward unless we look for more evidence that it does so. If after a long interval of time—let us say a million years after stopping all motion—the motion again started, we would never know about this interval unless we could make tests with our senses in some other way.

Hurwicz: That is a little bit like trying to tell if a train is moving without looking outside of the window.

Freier: Yes. We have to compare motions. In doing so, we have to look for some standard motion that is free from damping forces. One of the least damped motions that we have is our earth going around the sun. The motions of the moon going around the earth, the earth going around the sun, and the earth rotating on its own axis give us rather natural units of time: namely, the year due to the motion of the earth in its orbit, the month due to the motion of the moon in its orbit, and the day due to the motion of the earth rotating about its axis. We also have the other units of time like the hour, the minute, and the second. They are just convenient subdivisions.

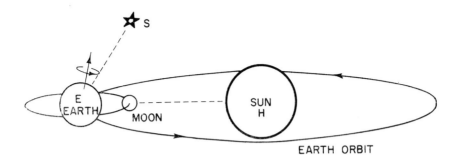

Now, let us take a closer look at these various motions. Since the most convenient motion to study is the rotation of the earth about its axis, our unit of time becomes the day. But to be more precise, we have two different kinds of days. There are fluctuations in the motion so we talk about a *mean solar day.*

What is a *mean solar day?* If I have a fixed star and if I draw a line from this star to the earth, the earth can rotate on its axis and an index point would cross the line, 366.2422 times in one sidereal year.

Hurwicz: It sounds as if you are a day off there. There are 365 days in a year.

Freier: The period of our rotational motion with respect to a fixed star is called a *sidereal day.* However, if I use the line from the earth to the sun as a reference, you will notice that, as the earth is rotating on its axis, our reference line is changing. This line to the sun completes its period of motion in one year so it adds one backward rotation of the earth in a year.

Trenerry: The earth in one year goes around the sun.

Freier: That is where we lose a day. We have only 365.2422 days in a year. Now, let's discuss the mean solar day. The motion of the earth about the sun in our model is a circular motion, but in nature it is an ellipse. Our reference line to the sun has a slightly irregular motion during the orbit of the earth about the sun.

Hurwicz: You mean different days have different durations.

Freier: Different days have slightly different durations because the imaginary reference line between the earth and sun is not moving uniformly in our solar system and we must average over the whole period. The average length of a day over one year is a mean solar day. Man has become so precise in his ability to tell time that, really, we cannot talk just about the mean solar day any more. There are perturbations on the earth's motion due to forces of other planets. As a result, scientists have chosen for this unit of time the *ephemeris second* which is a fractional part of the year 1900. We had to use a particular year, because other years are different from the year 1900. We are now, of course, looking for time determined from even freer systems.

Trenerry: Let me interrupt, professor. Could we not use astronomical reference points? We are tied to 365 days. The point you are trying to make is that we do not have to be.

Freier: We can, but the other common-sense thing is to use a fixed star for reference, and when we do that, we are back to a sidereal day.

Trenerry: I mean, can we use reference points without reference to the earth's rotation?

Freier: Yes, we could use other standard motions which exist on the earth. Let us take a look at another possible motion. Professor Hurwicz, perhaps you can see some standard motion that we might use in a bicycle-wheel?

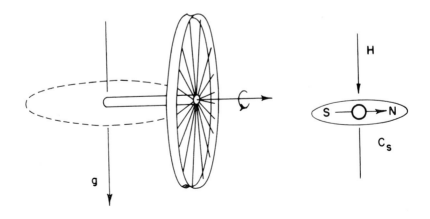

Hurwicz: I do not see any motion. It is just hanging loose so far, hanging by a string tied to its center.

Freier: We might look at it this way. First of all, if I hold the axle of the wheel horizontal, I think you see that it falls to a vertical position. Give the wheel a good spin and then hold the axis horizontal. Although it is held off the floor by a string, the axle does not fall down. It remains horizontal and the wheel precesses about a vertical axis.

Hurwicz: Sort of a gyro effect?

Freier: That is right. It's a gyroscope. I can sense the precession rate if I just swing the support a little bit at the same rate that the wheel is precessing. The wheel climbs or tends to flip over. In nature this motion can be used to tell time if we use cesium atoms as our gyroscopes. Cesium atoms, like many atoms, have built-in intrinsic spins, and are, consequently, intrinsic gyroscopes.

Hurwicz: You mean the nucleus itself is spinning?

Freier: Yes. The nucleus actually spins. This spin does not slow down like the gyroscope because it is a frictionless type of spin. It is present all the time. This kind of atom also has a magnetic moment, so I could put a torque on the atom by placing it in a magnetic field and consequently it would precess.

Hurwicz: Is it this spin that makes it into magnets?

Freier: That's right.

Mrs. Collins: Why are cesium atoms used?

Freier: Cesium atoms are used primarily because we do not want the atoms to interact with each other while they are carrying out the precessing motion. If they bump into each other, the motion is interrupted. Cesium atoms can be conveniently put into a beam where they won't interact with each other, and then the beam can pass through a magnetic field. This arrangement provides the freest system that we can conceive of with present knowledge.

Hurwicz: These atoms are not very sociable!

Freier: That's right. With this type of clock we can obtain more accuracy than with our old astronomical standard. In fact, this is now the new standard of time. We can hold this time accurately to within one part in 10 billion, which amounts to about one second in 300 years.

Collins: Does it have an advantage in space?

Freier: Yes, if we went out into space, we would lose our concept of the year, the month, and the day. They will all disappear. However, cesium atoms could be taken anywhere in space with us and would precess just as well out there.

Trenerry: Would we use the same reference points in space? You are using the cesium atom to define a second, aren't you? That is an earthly measurement.

Freier: No, it is not an earthly measurement. The cesium atom can precess about a magnetic field anywhere in space.

Trenerry: Well, how would you use this time standard on a trip to Mars? How would you describe it as a unit of time?

Hurwicz: I suppose in effect we would define the second in terms of the spinning cesium atom and our motion to Mars in terms of space intervals passed through in these intervals of time.

Freier: The year, the day, and the month would not be well defined concepts to us out in space. However, we could define them in terms of a certain number of seconds, since there are a certain number of seconds in a minute. The motion of the cesium atom would prescribe the standard second for us.

Hurwicz: You do not want to be dependent upon the sun rising.

Freier: That's right!

Collins: You do not want to be dependent on something that is like a pendulum in space.

Freier: In our laboratories we cannot all have cesium atom clocks or atomic clocks. We have a great number of secondary motions which can serve as secondary standards. I would like to point out that whenever we measure the frequency of a tuning fork, it is really some displacement or motion in space that we are measuring.

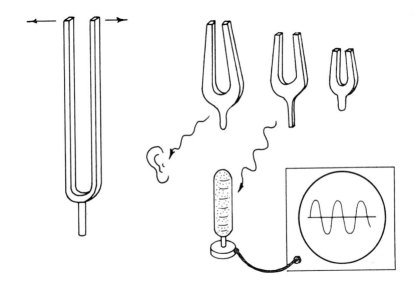

If I strike a low frequency tuning fork, you cannot hear it, but you can see or feel the motion. The frequency of the oscillation is too low to be heard.

Hurwicz: The motion is the vibration?

Freier: The motion is the vibration. A certain time interval elapses while the motion completes one of its cycles. If I use tuning forks which have higher frequencies, you hear the motion, but it is difficult to see any motion.

Again, we might take a tuning fork and, with the aid of a microphone, actually see its motion on the oscilloscope. If I hold the microphone up to the resonance box, you can see the motion as a wave motion on the oscilloscope.

Hurwicz: You mean waves on that oscilloscope screen correspond to the vibrations of the tuning fork?

Freier: The waves correspond to the vibration and, again, the distance between successive waves corresponds to units of time.

Hurwicz: When the motion slows down and peters out, don't the vibrations get slower also?

Freier: Ideally, of course, we would like them never to slow down, but there is a slight change, rather complicated—we won't go into the details. They do slow down a little bit, but they are still quite regular. I could intermittently drive the forks so that we could maintain the regular motion.

Collins: I have heard of quartz crystal being used as a measurement of time in somewhat the same way. Isn't that possible?

Freier: A quartz crystal can be used much the same way. In that particular case, the quartz crystal has a much higher natural frequency when excited. It will oscillate with a characteristic frequency which depends on its size. It can be driven by an electric force. You can put the electric forces on it in resonance with natural frequency of the quartz crystal. These vibrations usually have a much higher frequency than the tuning forks but they provide a good timing device.

For really accurate timing, listen to a radio station WWV in Washington, D.C. It broadcasts a signal which is determined by an atomic clock. If in our laboratories we want a good accurate measurement of time, we simply tune into station WWV.

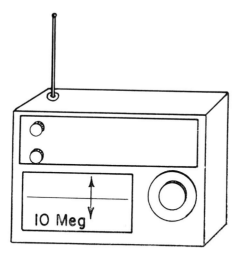

Hurwicz: Is that the U.S. Bureau of Standards source?

Freier: Yes. The signal consists of ticks which are just one second apart. There are many different time intervals given by this signal. The ticks are five cycles of a 1000 cycle pulse so each tick is 0.005 seconds long. At the end of each minute, one tick is omitted. The time is announced at each five-minute interval.

Hurwicz: Professor Freier, can anyone with a short-wave radio get this more accurate time signal?

Freier: Yes. There is a whole symphony of different frequencies presented, not very pleasing, but amazingly accurate.

Trenerry: What produces the sound?

Freier: The audible frequencies are produced by beating the higher frequencies from atomic clocks against each other. They have different oscillators and can very accurately produce practically any frequency they wish by beating two frequencies together.

Hurwicz: Professor Freier, when you originally started to tell us about the physicist's point of view, you said there are three concepts tied together. Time is the one we are interested in; one of the other two was space, which has brought us to this discussion of motion. The other one was mass. We have not seen yet what mass is and what it can do for our study of time.

Freier: How does mass get into the picture? We have several illustrations. We have been talking about motion, and time is very much involved with motion. At the beginning of the program I showed you a film and you agreed that maybe all motion could stop and we might not know it.

The physical scientist, however, would not really go along with this idea, because in order to stop we have to change the motion and if we change the motion, we must have accelerations. Accelerations of material points, of course, involve forces. You experience these forces when you change your motion by applying the brakes of your car. A body in motion tends to remain in motion. You usually tend to fly forward.

Hurwicz: It's a phenomena of inertia.

Freier: It's a phenomena of inertia, but the force originates because a material point has mass. Inertia is involved also when you start your car. A body at rest tends to remain at rest. It is the concept of mass that makes us believe that time is flowing along more or less uniformly. We think it must be moving smoothly, because if there were jerky motions in time, we would experience some large forces. A few demonstrations with mass will illustrate some important points.

These are reasonably heavy iron spheres tied to a handle. There is a string above each ball and a string below each ball. They are identical strings. If I pull down on one of the lower strings and keep pulling until the string breaks, which of the parts of the two strings—upper or lower—do you think will break? Maybe we can settle this democratically.

Collins: I guess the top one.

Freier: All right, I will just pull down gently. You're right. The top string broke. When I pulled down on it, that force was transmitted to the top string, but the top string also had to hold the weight of the ball so the top string broke.

Let's do the second one differently. Instead of pulling down gently this time, I am going to try to accelerate the mass by giving it a very fast downward jerk. If I pull down rapidly like this, the bottom string breaks. A body at rest tends to remain at rest.

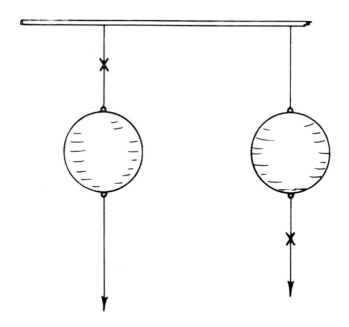

Hurwicz: The body in this case is the sphere. By holding back, it forces the bottom string to break.

Freier: That's right.

In another experiment we will again show that a body at rest tends to remain at rest. If I laid my hand on the table and hit it with this hammer, the hammer would be in motion and my hand would suffer severe injury. However, if I put a massive iron block on my hand, not only does my hand have to take the blow of the hammer, but it also has to hold up the heavy iron block.

Hurwicz: It sounds worse.

Freier: It sounds worse, but even if I give it a good hard blow, my hand is perfectly safe.

Collins: You try it.

Hurwicz: I did not know this was one of the duties of the host.

Freier: Simply lay your hand on the table. Then I will lay the block on top of it. I'll let you hit it if you want.

Hurwicz: It works. I still don't believe it. How heavy is this block?

Freier: It's quite heavy. It's an iron block.

Again, the point is that a body at rest tends to remain at rest. To summarize, if we *change* a motion, we have to experience big forces. In order to *stop* motion,

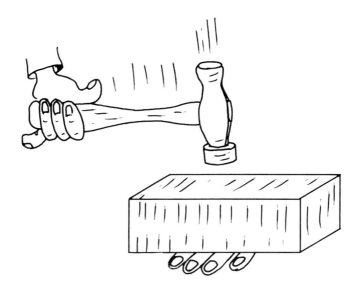

force is necessary, for if we simply remove forces from a body, it will keep on going in straight-line motion. In order to stop it we have to decelerate it, which requires force.

Hurwicz: How does this enter into the problem of time measurement?

Freier: We believe that our earth's motions are uniform because the accelerations due to non-uniform time don't exist.

Hurwicz: Then we feel more confident in using those motions as a basis for measurement of time.

Freier: That's right. The first of Newton's laws is that a body in motion tends to remain in motion, and a body at rest tends to remain at rest.

Trenerry: Do you think that it is impossible to have a concept of time based upon erratic motion?

Freier: I will show you some cases where we do have time defined in a statistical way which is quite erratic. We will talk about radioactive decay, leading to what we call half-lives. The decay of the radioactive nuclei is random. Its life is a statistical measurement so that, in this case, time could be called erratic. On the average, it flows rather continuously like all of these other standard motions.

Trenerry: I am not a physicist, but it seems to me that in quantum mechanics you base things on a series of jerks rather than on a smooth flow, which is supposed to be the underlining motion of the universe. Perhaps it is in such small quanta that we do not experience them as jerks when we see them.

Freier: The physicist is still worried about whether time is quantized or not. It turns out that in modern physics we have a large number of fundamental particles and each has a characteristic mass.

Hurwicz: The number is getting larger every year it seems.

Freier: More are found as time goes on. These fundamental particles nevertheless have discrete amounts of mass. Any one of these particles could be destroyed and converted into energy. When converted into energy, this energy shows up as a photon, that is, as Planck's constant times a frequency. (We have seen frequencies of the tuning forks.) Each discrete mass can be associated with a discrete frequency.

Hurwicz: That says that energy is quantized. Does it imply that time would be quantized?

Freier: Well, how do you measure the energy in this case? You measure it through frequency. That is, you measure time to measure energy.

Hurwicz: If time can come only in certain chunks and not otherwise, it is a minimum quantum.

Freier: It has been supposed that there may be a smallest unit of time, and some people have proposed the name *chronon.*

Trenerry: Wouldn't it work just as well as a measurement? After all, we are concerned about using something as a place from which to jump, aren't we? In other words, a fixed base is our time concept. Time must be in reference to something. Wouldn't these small particles do just as well as the rotation of the earth, for instance, which we are now using?

Freier: Yes, that would be a possible unit of time. In other instances we may destroy an electron and change it to a gamma ray or a photon.

Trenerry: You want something that's regular. When you find that something, you have your fixed base.

Freier: Also, it is necessary that it be convenient to use. That last method is not very convenient to use.

Again, going back to the idea of motion, what do you mean if you say you have a good watch? My watch, for instance, gains about ten minutes an hour and then it stops for ten minutes and in the average it comes out pretty well. Sometimes I may be late, however, and at other times I may be early.

Hurwicz: It's a good system if you can keep it up.

Freier: If, on the other hand, you have a good watch, it runs with a really uniform motion. The more money you pay, usually, the more uniform the motion and the better the watch.

For another experiment, I have a pendulum.

Hurwicz: Mrs. Collins was asking about the pendulum earlier.

Collins: Why won't this pendulum work in space?

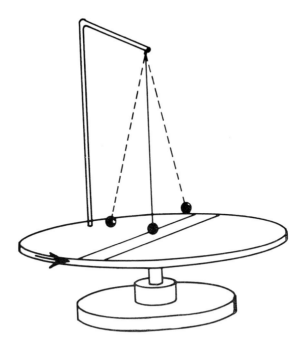

Freier: I have the pendulum swinging along a tape line across this platform and the platform is on a turntable. Let me ask *you* a question. If I turn the platform, will the pendulum keep swinging along this line? What do you think?

Hurwicz: I do not know. Maybe the ball will also change its orbit?

Freier: It could, but you notice it doesn't. It remains swinging in the same plane in space.
Suppose now that the platform is the surface of the rotating earth.

Hurwicz: It's flat but rotating.

Freier: That's right. Now, if I were viewing this pendulum from the surface of earth, I would not only say it was going back and forth, but I would say it was going in a circle too.

Hurwicz: It seems to me that I have seen something like that in a museum in San Francisco or somewhere. It really looks as if the pendulum were changing the direction in which it was moving; whereas, actually it proves that the earth is rotating.

Freier: We could do another experiment. Instead of my rotating the platform, we can start the pendulum along this line. The whole system is rotating because the earth's rotating. If we came back in a fraction of an hour we would see that the pendulum had rotated a little just as if I had turned the table.

Hurwicz: Then I suppose distance would be measured here and we would know what time it was. We could use that for telling time. It is essentially a clock.

Collins: In the United Nations building gravity is used to measure time.

Freier: The point is, the observer who was riding on earth would observe the added circular motion and he would say that there was a further acceleration. Then he would start to worry about all of the accelerations and what forces have produced them.

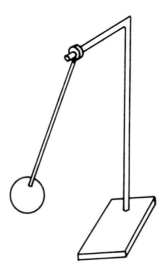

Here, again, I have a simple pendulum, which swings back and forth like a grandfather's clock. The period depends on the acceleration due to gravity at any point so that if it were taken to the North Pole, for instance, it would run a little bit faster than it would at the equator.

Hurwicz: Why would that be?

Freier: The gravitational force of the earth is approximately the same at the North Pole as at the equator, but the earth is rotating. At the equator we suffer a central acceleration and this central acceleration lengthens the period of the pendulum.

Hurwicz: It isn't related to the fact that the earth isn't quite spherical?

Freier: No, that isn't what I am talking about. There is some non-spherical effect too, but it's the acceleration that explains this phenomenon.

If an astronaut took one of these pendula into orbit, it would not work at all. Maybe we can test this idea. Let me just try throwing the pendulum and its support into the air.

Hurwicz: Let me evacuate the premises!

Freier: I can put the system into orbit momentarily by just throwing it upward. We see that the oscillations of the pendulum stop while it is in orbit. Of course, this is an orbit that quickly intersects the earth.

Hurwicz: I suppose this explains why space capsules don't have grandfather clocks.

Freier: Well, I suppose there are other reasons. In any case, it would be fruitless for them to take a grandfather clock. If you jumped out of the window with it, it would stop running. That doesn't mean you can live forever, though. We see that accelerations enter into the motions of some of our time-keeping devices. We know that our earth in its rotation produces an acceleration; the further motion around the sun is producing an acceleration. We know also that our solar system is moving through our galaxy, probably with accelerations. The various galaxies are probably accelerated with respect to each other. Therefore, when we want to properly orient ourselves in space, we have to consider stars that are so distant that we say the motion of the earth leaves them as fixed stars.

Hurwicz: Isn't that still somewhat relative? I mean that you can talk today about something that is fixed, but tomorrow somebody will find something that is a little more fixed.

Freier: Of course the accuracy of the measurement gets into this again. It seems we can always find further perturbing effects. Anyway, we are telling time in our laboratories. In the last analysis, time depends upon some star that is billions of light years away. This gets to be troublesome.

Hurwicz: Do you want to mention something about light years?

Freier: A light year is a distance, not a time. Light travels at a rate of 186,000 miles a second. In one year, there are close to 37 million seconds. If you multiply 186,000 by 37 million, you get the number of miles in a light year. It's a distance.

Hurwicz: In these units, the moon is a little over one light second away.

Freier: Let's return to the problem of how things are still interlocked with each other and tend to make the picture more confusing. Einstein took a new look at this problem. He said, let us suppose that there are just two observers in the universe. If one is moving he will have to move relative to the other. Each could say that he is fixed and the other one is moving relative to him.

Hurwicz: That is why they refer to this as the relativity theory.

Freier: This is relativity. We shall throw out the rest of the universe and just look at these two observers. I have a few charts which will place this idea on an historical basis. Let's suppose now that we have two earths: one which we might call our earth, writing its history, and another earth that is writing an identical history.

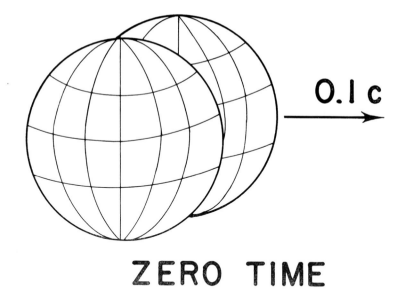

ZERO TIME

Hurwicz: They are like twins.

Freier: They are twin earths. Let's suppose now that they go by each other with one-tenth the velocity of light.

Hurwicz: Then speed is relative to one another.

Freier: Yes. Let's suppose that one earth is ours and that we are at rest with the other earth moving relative to us. In reality, we could say, also, that he is at rest and we are moving the other way.

Collins: Who is going to move?

Freier: For this example, we are going to stay at rest and write our history. The other earth is going to move off with one-tenth the velocity of light. Let's suppose that our paths crossed at the birth of Christ, which is the beginning of our present calendar.

Hurwicz: He is moving about 18,000 miles a second.

Freier: Yes. That's pretty fast, but we must assume this large speed if we are going to observe any appreciable effect.

Suppose this relative motion persists until 1775. The other planet then is 177.5 light years away from us. We now send a light signal to this planet to try to find out exactly what they are doing there, that is, where in time is their history? This signal is, of course, going ten times as fast as the planet but the planet has a 177.5 light year start. For a time, the planet continues to move with one-tenth the velocity of light, while the signal travels with the velocity of light.

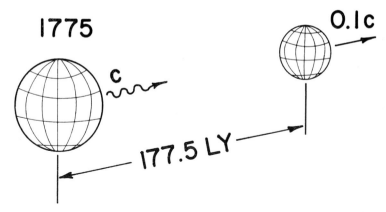

We then have a simple equation: ct = 0.1 ct + 177.5 c. When you solve this equation we find that t = 197 years, or that it takes 197 years for the signal to go from us to the planet.

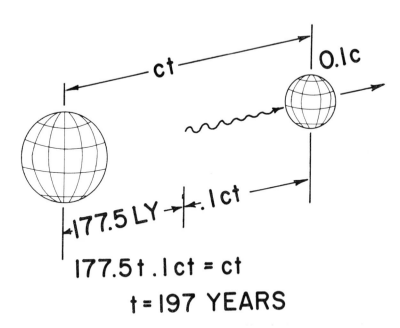

177.5 t . l ct = ct

t = 197 YEARS

Hurwicz: The reason it's more than 177 is that while the signal is going, even at this tremendous speed, the other planet is getting away a little further. You have to allow an extra 20 years just for that.

Freier: Yes. Suppose that as soon as the signal arrives, they turn on a tremendous computer, which can immediately relay all their history back to us on a return signal which requires another 197 years to return to us.

Hurwicz: That would be stop-the-press news.

Freier: Yes. They send a signal back to us which contains information about all their history. We sent the signal in 1775; it took 197 years to get there. We would calculate that it will arrive at our twin earth in 1972, and that their history should be written in the year 1972.

Hurwicz: In other words, when we get the news back, we—or our grandchildren—will know what happened in 1971.

Freier: Of course, it will take 197 years to get back so we won't know about this until 2169.

Collins: We had better get busy. . . .

Hurwicz: It's about 204 years from now.

Freier: It would arrive back here in 2169.

Hurwicz: The most recent data that we would get would be 1972.

Freier: Our calculations so far show that we would get data up to 1972. However, the relativist would look at this in a slightly different way. He would say that these times have to follow a certain transformation law. That is, I have to be able to determine the year 2169 from the year T^1 for the moving observer in the same way that the moving observer determines T^1 from the year 1775.

$$\begin{array}{r} 1775 \\ 197 \\ \hline 1972 \end{array}$$ SIGNAL SENT

ARRIVAL TIME

$$\begin{array}{r} 1972 \\ 197 \\ \hline 2169 \end{array}$$

RETURN OF SIGNAL

Hurwicz: We have sort of two separate time tracks.

Freier: That's right. The fellow on the other earth should determine the year when our signal arrives, which I have called Y^1, from the year 1775, by a certain multiplying factor. By the symmetry of the problem, I should be able to determine the year 2169 from the year Y^1 in exactly the same way that I determined Y^1 from 1775. The problem must be symmetric since there is only relative motion between the observers.

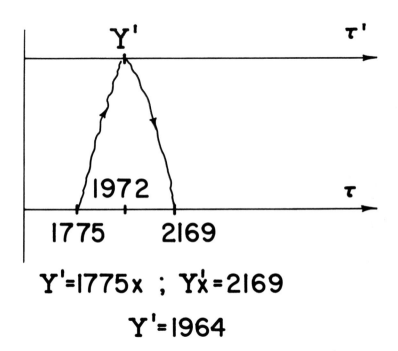

Hurwicz: The ratio of 1775 to Y^1 is the same as of Y^1 to 2169.

Freier: Yes, I have written that as two equations: $1775x = Y^1$ and $Y^1x = 2169$. If you solve that for the year Y^1, it comes out 1964.

Hurwicz: So we lose eight years' worth of information.

Freier: The relativist would say that the latest history that we would get would not be 1972 but would be 1964. In this sense now, the moving clock is running more slowly.

Hurwicz: You mean the speed of passage of time depends on whether you are standing still or moving and how fast?

Freier: That's right. I can do similar experiments in the laboratory that bring out the results of special relativity. One experiment that is not so direct, of course, is the idea of the Doppler shift. It comes out of relativity but it's quite indirect. Suppose someone on the other planet were carrying a tuning fork which was oscillating at 500 cycles per second. We would hear a frequency of 450 cycles per second; that is, we would experience what we call a red shift. Frequencies are slowed down as the planet moves away from us at a high velocity.

Hurwicz: It's like the sound of a locomotive whistle. Depending upon whether the train is coming or going, it goes up or down.

Trenerry: Is that a natural change or a change in the observer?

Freier: It's a real change. I can measure a certain signal on the ground at rest, and then put that same transmitter up on a satellite. I can tell whether it is moving away from me or moving towards me by the frequency.

Collins: Getting back to the train whistle. When you hear it a long way off it's higher than when it is very close. There is a switch not in the volume but in the pitch.

Freier: It isn't because it is far away or close. It depends upon whether the source of sound is coming towards you or going away from you. You will hear a high-pitch sound as the object approaches, and just as it goes by, the pitch drops.

Collins: It is very noticeable.

Hurwicz: Yet, from the sender's point of view it remains constant.

Freier: That's true. It is indirect proof, but it comes out of relativity theory. It could, however, come out of other theories, also.

Collins: So we have to believe that a moving clock runs more slowly.

Freier: Well, there are much better checks. A meson, for example, which is produced in a laboratory, will exist as an entity only a very short time.

Hurwicz: What sort of thing is a meson?

Freier: That's one of the strange particles which we were talking about earlier. It will live about one one-millionth of a second.

Hurwicz: One-millionth of a second!

Freier: Yes, just one-millionth of a second. If these mesons are produced in our upper atmosphere, and if they live one-millionth of a second, and they can move with a speed no greater than 300 million meters per second, they should be able to travel no further than 300 meters. You would expect that in its lifetime, one of them could go a distance of 300 meters.

Hurwicz: That is because it lives only one-millionth of a second?

Freier: That's right. At the surface of the earth however, we are probably 30,000 meters below the point of creation, and we can still find these mesons. Now, how do you explain the fact that they should have all decayed by the time they reached the surface of the earth?

Hurwicz: They sneaked through somehow?

Freier: Their moving clock is running slower—their clock is their lifetime.

Collins: They live a little longer than we would expect because they are moving with a high speed.

Freier: They are moving very close to the velocity of light.

Hurwicz: I have a question about longevity. I once read a story that seems quite fanciful about what would happen to twin brothers if one of them remained on earth and the other one went into space with the tremendous speed of light, traveled quite a bit and came back later, at a time when his earthly twin was, perhaps, 60 years old. According to this story, the relativity theory tells us that the brother who had traveled at this great speed actually would not have aged to the same extent.

Freier: You have to believe that story. There is one thing, however, that complicates your situation so that it does not fit the theory well. Remember that we had a planet going away from us. It could have been either going *away* from or toward us, but only one or the other. However, if I am going to go both away from and towards my starting point, I have to suffer a tremendous acceleration somewhere along the line. This theory of relativity, however, is not good for accelerated systems. It is, however, good for systems moving with uniform relative velocities.

Hurwicz: You mean it's a special theory of relativity.

Freier: Yes. Even so, the general theory of relativity would allow us to calculate the results for your problem.

Hurwicz: Are the twins still aging differently, even in general relativity?

Freier: That's right.

Trenerry: Don't forget the laws of physiology. You are talking about concepts, not people, now.

Freier: I am talking about people. The life processes are exactly the same sort of thing. They obey the laws of physics.

Trenerry: I wouldn't doubt that. Yet I would doubt that there would be any change.

Freier: According to the theory, they would change.

Let us move on now. We talked about time going, or flowing on. Usually people think of time as the past and the future. We should say a little bit about the equations of physics which tell us, when we solve them for most of these experiments, that time could go backwards as well as forwards. We could put in negative values of time and the process would simply go backward.

Hurwicz: Is that like running a movie backward?

Freier: That's right. We can determine the past from the present as well as the future from the present. We can solve all the differential equations of motion but the solutions will not tell us which way time is going.

Hurwicz: Suppose you were running a movie. First you ran it forward, then backward. Suppose an observer did not know which was forward and which was backward. How could he tell which way time was progressing?

Freier: The physicist would talk about it in a different way. He would say that he has to write down a differential equation for some process and then solve the differential equation. He could solve it for negative time as well as for positive time. In reality we don't know whether we are going or coming.

Collins: Well. I think I do.

Freier: You do, but the person solving the differential equation doesn't.

Here I have another little experiment, using an oscilloscope. When I flick this switch you will see on the oscilloscope this periodic motion—the wiggly lines—that we have been talking about.

Hurwicz: It's flicking. Did you plug in some current?

Freier: Yes. I want you to observe that we are getting characteristic wiggles like a frequency. What I would also like to point out is that we have an order/disorder process that tells us which way time is going. As time goes on, our universe is becoming more and more disordered. It goes from a state of order to disorder.

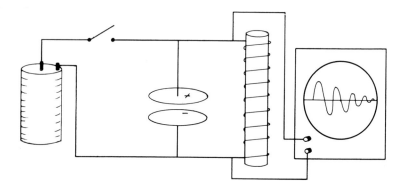

This demonstration does it in the following way. The battery puts charge on the condenser in an ordered way. That is, it puts positive charge in one plate and negative charge on the other plate of the condenser.

Hurwicz: By order you mean a definite differentiation of attributes.

Freier: Yes. I sort the charge so that one charge sign is on one plate and the other sign is on the other plate. I've got everything in good order.

Now, when I release this switch, I am disconnecting the battery, and what you see on the oscilloscope then is the charge running back and forth through the inductance. That charge can go back and forth through the inductance and make those wiggly lines. If there were no resistance in this circuit, those wiggly lines would retain their same amplitude, the same height on the oscilloscope. Due to the fact that there is resistance, the two different kinds of charge are getting mixed up; the positive and negative charge are combining and soon there will be no net charge left.

Hurwicz: That is why the lines on the oscilloscope converge.

Freier: Observe the decaying nature of the trace on the oscilloscope. It has a very characteristic shape and shows that it takes a certain amount of time for the oscillation process to decay. We call that a relaxation time. The nature of this relaxation time tells us that there is more disorder in the universe after the discharge than there was before. We say, then, that time is running in the direction from order to disorder.

Hurwicz: Disorder you equate with randomness, more or less?

Freier: That's right. Disorder is randomness.

Collins: That has nothing to do with half-life?

Freier: Yes it does.

Let us take a look quickly at that experiment over here. We have a device which shows another example of exactly the same idea. I have a nuclear particle counter and a scaler. If I bring this sample up to the counter, you can see the little lights flash and you can hear the ticks.

What is happening is that atoms of the sample are decaying and sending out particles to this particular counter in a statistical sort of way. If I would come back in a certain length of time, the rate at which I would get the counting would be less than it is now. In the case of uranium, if I came back four and a

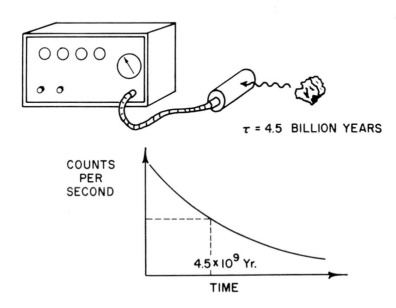

τ = 4.5 BILLION YEARS

COUNTS PER SECOND

4.5×10^9 Yr.

TIME

half billion years from now, the counting rate would be half of what it is now. So, again, we have this relaxation time which can be used as a clock.

Hurwicz: You talk about this as being somewhat random and statistical. We have heard on one of these programs how archaelogists find this sort of measurement accurate enough to date the Egyptian mummies and a variety of other things with very considerable accuracy.

Freier: They can do it, but they would have to take a large number of counts. Timing gets more and more accurate as we take more and more counts. If I just took two counts, for instance, I couldn't measure time, since the counts are completely random. If I take a million counts, I can determine the average counting rate very accurately. What one does is determine counting rate on a graph. When the counting rate drops to half its value, we say that the one half-life has gone by, one half-life of the atoms. With uranium it is four and one half billion years; with carbon-14 it is fifty-six hundred years.

Hurwicz: That means that half of it has decayed, but not that it has lived out half of its life exactly.

Freier: Half of it has decayed.

Collins: So we can tell time by biological processes as well?

Freier: That's right. By biological processes, for instance, we could determine the population of a metropolitan area by watching its birth rate or its death rate. We might wonder why there is all this fuss about the accuracy in time.

Hurwicz: Is this just to please the physicists?

Freier: Well, I think the social scientists probably get into the act, too.

I have just one more quick little demonstration. This is again a model of the earth which is rotating on its axis. The axis stays fixed in space. Now for a

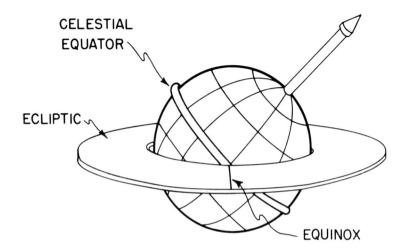

moment, let's imagine the earth at rest and suppose that the sun moves around in the ecliptic once a year. The sun seems to go around this path once a year if we consider the earth at rest. The path of the sun—the ecliptic—and the celestial equator intersect in two points which we call the equinoxes. Due to interaction of the earth with other planets and the sun, the spinning earth precesses to make the position of an equinox change as time goes on.

Hurwicz: The axis doesn't always point at the same solar star?

Freier: No, it doesn't. The earth precesses once around in a period of about twenty-five thousand years. Now, most of our astrology tables, for instance, depend upon the signs of the zodiac. When the earth precesses, the equinox occurs at different signs of the zodiac. The astrologers use tables constructed by the Babylonians.

Hurwicz: That was several thousands of years ago.

Freier: It was about two thousand years ago. In two thousand years the earth has precessed one zodiacal sign. So the tables are all wrong.

Hurwicz: This sounds very serious.

Freier: We know many things that have been done in history were based on readings of the signs of the zodiac. Hitler and many rulers called in their astrologers to make their big decisions. It would be interesting to see how different history would be if they had made their decisions more accurately.

The other big use is in navigation. By telling accurate time, we can tell where we are on the earth. If you leave here and go to California without changing your watch, you will notice that your watch is two hours fast and you will know how far around the earth you are. Good timepieces made navigation possible for a lot of people other than geniuses like Christopher Columbus who could do it all by dead-reckoning.

Hurwicz: Let's try to summarize the points we have learned from this discussion and the various exhibits. It seems to me that one basic point that was made was that we shouldn't be talking about time alone, because one has to discuss time—at least as far as the physicist is concerned—in its relation to space and mass.

Another point is this very remarkable accuracy which the physicist gets down to when he talks about one-millionth of a second or one-billionth of a second, and still can distinguish those two.

Finally, I found extremely interesting the aspect of relativity theory which makes the social scientists feel somewhat vindicated because it turns out that there is a subjective aspect in physics and time measurement in spite of the great accuracy. The observer has to be taken into account. Of course, that is precisely what the social scientists and philosophers primarily take into account. They are interested in the perception of time.

Time and Human Knowledge

What connection might a philosopher see between time and human knowledge and memory?

SPEAKER: *D. BURNHAM TERRELL*, PROFESSOR OF PHILOSOPHY

COMMENTATORS: *ROBERT H. BECK*, PROFESSOR OF THE HISTORY AND PHILOSOPHY OF EDUCATION
BRYCE CRAWFORD, JR., PROFESSOR OF CHEMISTRY AND DEAN OF THE GRADUATE SCHOOL

Professor Hoyt: It is now three seconds after one minute after 9:00 p.m.—I think. At least that's the Central Standard Time here in St. Paul; It's something else in Minneapolis. Daylight Time? In any case it is very timely tonight that our main speaker is a professor of philosophy. Philosophy is a discipline that deals with eternal truths, according to some of the older philosophers, at least. Perhaps it could be argued that anything to do with eternal truth by definition excludes the factor of time. Surely, the philosopher might be asked to defend his interest in time. Professor Terrell, how about beginning by telling us why or how the philosopher is concerned with aspects of time?

Professor Terrell: Well, Stuart, philosophers have been concerned with time for a long time. As a matter of fact, watching last week's program with Professor Freier, I was reminded by his opening remarks of a view about time which has a very distinguished history. Professor Freier was, in his comments about time and motion, reiterating the view adopted by the first writer of a systematic work on physics, Aristotle. In his work, *Physics*, Aristotle said, nearly 2,400 years ago, that time is the number of movement according to before and after. This was, I think you will recall, essentially the view about time and movement of which Professor Freier was speaking in the introduction to his talk on time and measurement.

We have to go back before Aristotle, even before Plato and Socrates, to get at the beginnings of the philosopher's treatment of time. We find very early in ancient philosophy two strongly contrasting views about time, change, and reality.

The earlier was that represented by Heraclitus of Ephesus[1] in Asia Minor, who held the doctrine that has become principally identified with him. The doctrine says that "all things flow." Everything flows and nothing abides. Perhaps the most famous saying of Heraclitus was that "you cannot step twice into the same river, for other waters are continually flowing on." Here is an illustration of such a unique episode in history, Heraclitus stepping into the river, the one time it is possible. He will never be able to step into that same river twice, as he tells us.

---

[1] Wheelwright, Philip E., *Heraclitus* (Princeton, 1959).

Professor Crawford: Didn't someone say that you can't step in the same river even once?

Terrell: Yes. Over on the other side of the river on the shore is Cratylus, who, as a matter of fact, has no business being in the same picture at all, because he came considerably later than Heraclitus. They weren't contemporaries, but he was a Heraclitean. Aristotle, among others, tells us that Cratylus drew a still more radical conclusion from Heraclitus' doctrine that everything flows, and all things are continually changing. His conclusion was that you cannot step into the same river once.[2] You see, though he is dressed for bathing, there is an expression of chagrin on his face, for he has just now concluded that it is after all impossible, if everything flows, to step into the same river even one time.

The point is, of course, that if there is nothing but change, we can no longer talk about sameness or identity; so the very concept of the same river in a world of nothing but change becomes incoherent.

Professor Beck: Did anybody challenge this work?

Terrell: Well, as a matter of fact, I was suggesting earlier that two very sharply contrasting views had developed. The answer to your question about a challenge

---

[2] Aristotle, *Metaphysics* Book IV, Ch. 5, 1010a, 12-14.

to the Heraclitean view of complete flow is to be found in the Eleatic school, of which the founder and leader, was Parmenides.[3] The view of Parmenides and the Eleatics generally was the exact contrary of the Heraclitean view; namely, nothing changes. Reality is the one which is eternally the same. There is no change, no multiplicity. There is only the one; that which is.

However, the most famous representative of the Eleatic school, which denied the meaningfulness of change, was Zeno. Zeno[4] invented some arguments, known as Zeno's Paradoxes, to prove that this view is correct, that time and change are impossible.

I want to illustrate a couple of these paradoxes. The picture I am going to show you is of the famous race between Achilles and the Tortoise. Zeno invented this contest as an illustration of what happens to the concept of time if you consider time and space to be infinitely divisible.

In the illustration, we see Achilles about to begin his race with the tortoise; the tortoise has been given a head-start. There he is well out in front of Achilles. Now, what Zeno set out to do with the paradox—the Achilles paradox—was to show that if there are an infinite number of points in time or along a line, it would be impossible for Achilles to catch the tortoise.

We'll check from time to time on the progress of Achilles and the Tortoise. Right now, consider another of Zeno's arguments, the paradox of the arrow, which was intended to prove that motion is impossible when time and space are divided not infinitely but into minute pieces. The two paradoxes are comple-

FINISH   START

mentary. One is directed at the idea of motion in infinitely divisible space and time, the other at motion in time and space composed of ultimate points and instants.

Pictured on the next page is an arrow at randomly selected moments of its supposed flight. You can see different moments in the life of the arrow. Since these pictures are random selections from the so-called flight of the arrow, and the arrow is at rest in each of them, then there is no instant of the arrow's

---

[3] F. M. Cornford (ed. and tr.) *Plato and Parmenides* (New York: Liberal Arts Press, 1957).

[4] H. D. P. Lee (ed. and tr.) *Zeno of Elea* (Cambridge: The University Press, 1936).

flight when it is not at rest; hence, the very concept of the flying arrow has been shown to be impossible. The flying arrow is not really flying at all, but at every instant of its flight, as shown in the pictures, is at rest.

Crawford: Burnham, how do you see that it is at rest? How did Zeno see that it is at rest? With a modern framing camera you can almost do this. It looks as if it were at rest.

Terrell: The camera won't do it because the camera won't catch it at a precise instant.

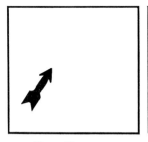  

FIRST POSITION   SECOND POSITION   THIRD POSITION

Crawford: Exactly. So it is never at rest.

Terrell: An artist drew the pictures . . .

Crawford: Then, they are not real. In fact, it is really not at rest.

Terrell: They show where the arrow really is at one precise instant of its flight.

Crawford: But there is no such thing.

Terrell: I modified Zeno's argument a little bit, in fact. He wrote about the arrow occupying the same space as itself. Anything that occupies the same space as itself at a given time is at rest. Now, at any particular instant, the arrow can't be at two different places, because there is just the one instant. There is no further divisibility. Remember, this is the form of the argument directed to the view that time and space are composed of discrete and indivisible instants and points.

Beck: Didn't anyone refute the paradoxes?

Terrell: Well, there have been countless efforts toward resolving Zeno's paradoxes, some of them involving complicating mathematical apparatus. However, the simplest, most straight-forward refutation is the origin of the expression, *"solvitur ambulando"*—"it is solved by walking." The refutation is attributed to Diogenes, but then, so are most such clever moves.

(Walking back and forth) So much for the possibility of motion: *Solvitur ambulando.*

Beck: That is not the only level of experience.

Crawford: It's a bit more operational.

Terrell: It was not the most devastating reply to Zeno. It was the simplest and most straightforward.

Crawford: It has no logic in it, just terribly witty and convincing.

Beck: You know, some people in education still take these ideas quite seriously. Some people pay a lot of attention to change, management, and the future. They think that what is true is true and will always be true for all people for all time.

Crawford: Others say that actually we are and should be constantly in a state of change.

Terrell: Well, actually, of course, we've been talking about change and motion, which are implicitly time, especially because time has a connection with motion, but what we set out to talk about really is time and human knowledge. These arguments are concerned with the reality and the nature of time. I want to turn our attention from the problem of the existence of time and change to the problem of man's knowledge of change, because there are some interesting questions the philosopher has to deal with in this connection.

Crawford: You mean we shall not worry about whether there is such a thing as change. We say Diogenes settled the question and we recognize change.

Terrell: We know change. The important thing to note is that it is not sufficient for there to be change and for us to know both parts of the change—what is first and then what follows it—because that would not provide an awareness of the change itself. Two different awarenesses one after the other, are not quite enough for an awareness of change. You have to have, as it is put sometimes, not just a succession of awarenesses, but an awareness of succession.

Crawford: Wait a minute! What you are saying is that you not only have to have cognition of two separate events, but to know that one is before the other.

Terrell: That would do it. It is not enough to know two separate events, to know one and then know the other. These two bits of knowledge can be entirely disconnected, you see.

Crawford: But you have to know that one comes before the other.

Terrell: Take, for example, a simple illustration of a very primitive awareness of change. Suppose you looked up at the wall and saw a light go on. When the light went on we were not only aware of the light, but, I think one could say, aware of light beginning. In other words, we have the awareness of the light, and the awareness of the light just having appeared in a place where there was no light. At the same time, if the light should go off, the awareness of that spot is an awareness of a place where a light was, where a light just ended. Of course, if the light goes on again, then, we have somewhat a more complicated kind of awareness, one that is very relevant to the concept of time. We can say, there is that same light again.

We are aware of repetition; we see the light not just going on, but being that same light we saw before. There is a recognition involved that leads us closer to the concepts of before and after.

Now, if you looked toward the other side of the room, you might have another kind of awareness—there is light there after light here. This is an awareness of change in position, change in place. Now we are using concepts of before and after.

My point is that in each case we weren't just aware of a light; we were aware of a light beginning, aware of that same light again, aware of light now here that used to be there. All of these involve not just the awareness of the immediate instant, but a reference in that awareness to something else.

Of course, as we become more clear in our thinking, more directly concerned with the nature of what was before, we can start to talk about remembering. We can direct our attention to what there was before, and then we are talking about memory. Of course, what is interesting about memory is that we have one present awareness for reference not only to what there is now, but to something that isn't there any more.

Crawford: You mean that the present awareness includes not only what we now perceive but also the recollection of numbers of things past.

Terrell: Yes, we have in some sense the past, the memory, projected in or represented in the present. It's a temporal awareness.

Beck: It is the remembrance of things past. How about Achilles? I wonder how the race is going.

Terrell: Achilles has not gotten to the point where the tortoise started from. If the tortoise had stayed there, Achilles would have caught the tortoise, but the

FINISH   START

tortoise hasn't stayed there. He hasn't caught the tortoise yet. We will check again later.

Let's go back to remembering. We have in the present awareness of something present. There is also reference to the past involved in it. Of course, there is no need in our discussion of time before and after to restrict ourselves to the relationship between present and past, or expectation, present and future, because we can make judgments about temporal relationships of things which are both in the past. Think of the American Revolution having been before the French Revolution. We are thinking about two events and we give them a temporal relationship, yet neither one of them is in the present. Nevertheless, all of this presupposes some of those more primitive awarenesses of change and time of which we were talking before.

One of the interesting things that artists—some of the artists of this century, especially—have attempted to do is to give an artistic representation to this peculiar feature of our temporal consciousness. They attempt in the work of art to give visually, or pictorially, at the same time, different temporal phases of our experience. For example, there are attempts to show all at once the various phases of a movement. One of the most familiar of the examples is in Marcel Duchamp's famous picture, "Nude Descending the Stairs," in which the figure is seen not just at one time, but all at once throughout the episode of descending the stairs.

Hoyt: Some of us will have to take this on faith.

Terrell: It doesn't look like a nude descending the stairs, to be sure. The idea is to combine all the different phases of the motion to one visual image, just as in memory we somehow hold all the different phases of the movement together.

Marcel Duchamp's (1887-   ), "Nude Descending the Stairs," *a staircase* 1912 (original in color).

That is the idea represented. The other way in which this simultaneous presentation of separate phases of our experience occurs is when we are presented by the artist with diffrent *views* we could never have literally at the same time.

Here we have another famous contemporary painting, Picasso's "Girl Before the Mirror." You notice that typical Picasso trick of showing both the full face and the profile in the same picture in the same visual image. What the artist is trying to do is to present visually in one image the same feature of temporal experience. I was calling to your attention in the case of memory and temporal judgment, having in consciousness at one time an awareness of things that are separate in real time.

Crawford: Now, let us see. In the case of the "Nude Descending the Stairs," we have a simultaneous representation of several different points of view in time, so to speak. In the Picasso, you had more than one viewpoint geometrically, so to speak. It's the same view but you have to scuttle around.

Terrell: It's changed. In one case, it is the thing which is changed, the position of the figure on the stairs. In the other case, it's the same, unchanging girl before the mirror, but the viewer's position varies. This is, in fact, oversimplification,

Pablo Picasso's (1881-   ) "Girl Before a Mirror," 1932 (original in color).

to put it mildly, of Picasso's painting, but for our purposes, it will serve to illustrate the idea that our awareness of the same unchanging thing itself changes. We see it now from this point of view, now from another point of view.

In thinking of a person, or the appearance of a person, our memory is not restricted to just one view, but combines them all. Consider your visual image of someone familiar to you. If you have that kind of capacity for imagining— I don't; I don't have very good imagery, but I suppose if you did—you would be able to think of different visual images of that person and you would not be too concerned about what you literally saw first, profile or full face. The total visual image of her might very well include the recollection of profile and full face as well. Whether they would be combined in exactly the way as in Picasso's painting, I can't say.

Beck: How would you check on this, Burnham? How would you know if it was accurate or not or would that not make any difference?

Terrell: I don't think the usual sense of accuracy and representation would here hold because, really, we never get this kind of literally simultaneous—I am talking about memory, including both of these phases. Obviously, I think even some of them with a very vivid capacity for visual imagery would probably not have something which does or does not like Picasso's painting.

Crawford: I don't want to drag in any red herring, but I don't know. Did you mean, Bob, to bring in the question that if you and I and even our moderator, Stuart, all saw the same succession of events and then recalled them and described them to each other we might find ourselves embroiled in an argument?

Beck: We might.

Terrell: There is a sort of metaphysical counterpart to the artistic representation of what is involved in our temporal awareness. Philosophers have often been led to conclude that all the events constituting time or history have to be there to be real, because in memory we have not only the awareness of the present time but this reference to something past. They say we can't just be thinking of nothing when we are remembering the past. The past must be there somehow to be thought of. This is one consideration that leads philosophers to judge that the events that constitute history are, in a sense, real.

Hoyt: Isn't this an act of faith? Memory is now, in the present, even though the object of the memory has passed. What connects the present memory now with the past thing remembered? There has to be something external to the mind that serves to convince oneself that what one remembers is not a chimera but a reality. We make a generalization, an extrapolation, because most of the important things the four of us would remember jibe pretty well. Well, we say, it must have been true.

Crawford: Is this what you were referring to, the act of faith, a generalization, an extrapolation? Were you speaking of the faith we have when we say this really happened?

Terrell: I am speaking of veridical memory; memory which is true, memory of things that really happened.

Crawford: Is it personal? Does it have to be in my memory?

Terrell: Yes.

Crawford: Well, I don't know anything about Napoleon, let's say, or de Gaulle.

Terrell: No, you don't remember Napoleon, surely, in the sense with which we are now concerned. You know some things about Napoleon. As a matter of fact, this is the next move one might make, because even though you do not remember Napoleon, and the special problems about the relationship that memory seems to involve between yourself and your own past, still, there are things we know about Napoleon. We know his date; we know that he ruled after the French Revolution. What I am driving at is that there *are* temporal facts which involve Napoleon.

Crawford: We know this only by Bob's act of faith.

Terrell: Suppose we know this; assume that we know it to be true. What are we obliged to conclude from it? There are facts *now* in which Napoleon is an element. Napoleon comes before us and after George Washington. We can order Napoleon in time and so we can say that if Napoleon can presently be related to someone else as before or after, then Napoleon must, in some sense, be.

Beck: There must be facts to compound more truths.

Crawford: We all find it the easiest way to order our lives. To say that where there is general agreement upon memories, where there is a general agreement on an extrapolation, then we say, yes, there was a fellow by the name of Napoleon. Because of him the sugar-beet industries exist, or things of this sort.

Hoyt: We say that something existed where there is general agreement concerning the meaning of data surviving from the past, which brings us back to the present or Now and makes us no longer dependent upon memory.

Crawford: There are always other explanations. We do not believe them because they are more complicated, or we don't like them, or they are ugly—I mean esthetically ugly and therefore not convincing. Well, let us not delude ourselves that philosophy is logic.

Terrell: Supposing we do have knowledge of historical facts, what follows from this? What some philosophers, metaphysicians have claimed is that it follows from this that somehow all the events that constitute history must be there, must be real, even now, because there are facts about them. There are facts now; there must be some reality to the events they relate.

This generates what I call the tableau or the panorama theory of time, in which one conceives of time of history as a great panorama in which all the events are laid out. They are there for all time. What this means is a return essentially to the Eleatic view. If these things are here all the time, change seems to have disappeared. The problem emerges, for the metaphysician of how to restore to reality the Heraclitean flow.

Naturally, there are two metaphors—two kinds of metaphors—that metaphysicians have attempted to introduce here. We could call one of them "the-moving-event" sort of metaphor. There is a panorama. Let the panorama flow past a point which is called Now. So the events that haven't gotten there, the parts of the whole series which have not yet passed are still future. The ones that have already passed by it are the past. This, of course, is very adaptable to the river metaphor.

A more contemporary version of the flowing or moving events theory would be represented by the motion-picture projector. The projector serves as the Now and the film is history or the string of events that constitutes history. As the film flows from one reel onto the other, all the events on the one reel constitute the future. Once they are taken past the projector and onto the other reel they become the past. It offers a convenient contemporary, technological counterpart for the flowing events metaphor represented historically by Heraclitus' river.

The other sort of metaphor I am interested in we might call "the moving Now" metaphor. The British philosopher, C. D. Broad, had a version of the moving Now metaphor.[5] On his version of it, time or history is like a street of houses and Now is the light of a bull's eye lantern which illuminates first one house down the street, and then the next, and so on.

Now, here we have in our picture a street of houses. I will turn on the Now light. Stuart, would you like to explain as an historian just where Now is at this time.

Most historians would agree that this is a caveman's split-level of about 20,000 B.C. Ordinary houses on a street would have addresses identifying their positions spatially on the street. The houses on C. D. Broad's temporal street have dates for addresses. Flow is introduced into the panorama of events by having the point called Now move along.

Hoyt: We can move the Now past this stone castle, this Tudor townhouse of 1492, the hill with the flag bearing the date 1776, the southern plantation of 1861, and of course for 1965, our address date, a modern split-level.

Terrell: Then we continue to move on . . .

---

[5] *Scientific Thought,* p. 59.

Hoyt: Some historians would conjecture this date to be about 2000 A.D. This dwelling would be a reversion to cave-like living—a bomb shelter adorned by an ultra high-frequency television antenna on top.

Terrell: George Santayana had a different metaphor, rather a vivid one: "The essence of Now runs like a fire along the fuse of time." That, too, is of course a "moving Now" metaphor, like C. D. Broad's.

These various metaphors in connection with the panorama view of time have led to some fairly interesting speculations about time and human knowledge. I would not want to give them any philosophical endorsement. I bring them in here not so much because I think there is very much truth in them, but because they are the kind of speculations that are likely to emerge out of the conception of time as a panorama of events—a conception which has, in turn, emerged out of our original conception of what our temporal awareness and our temporal knowledge involve.

Crawford: You spoke of this as a speculation. This is really a second generalization or act of faith—to borrow Stuart's medieval and very modern term. It's a second act of faith on top of the first act of faith. The first act of faith is that these things which we corporately remember did exist and were real. The second act of faith, if you will, is that we think of them as a tableau or river which either flows past us or along which we move.

Hoyt: I wonder if it would be time to check on the progress of Achilles and the tortoise? Achilles is gaining. I wonder where the tortoise is.

FINISH   START

Terrell: He has arrived where the tortoise was, but the tortoise isn't there any more. And so, he still hasn't caught the tortoise. You know, I think it's going to go on like this. It would take an infinite time because every time Achilles arrives where the tortoise was, the tortoise has moved on, and this goes on without end, so I am afraid if we are going to wait for Achilles to catch the tortoise, we will have to wait an infinitely long time. We don't have that much time.

Beck: There is something dissatisfactory about that picture, but I haven't figured it out.

Hoyt: Another thing that bothers me concerns this tableau of a few minutes ago. We have all this knowledge, but historians talk only about knowledge of the past;

yet, on the tableau, we ended up in 2000 A.D. Is there such a thing as knowledge of the future?

Terrell: This is part of our subject. It introduces the possibility of the kind of speculation I was talking about, which was opened up by the panorama theory. As long as the events are all there, just because Now moves along at its slow, steady pace, there is no reason why we shouldn't speculate on the possibility of getting ahead of Now in our cognition. In this speculation human knowledge goes ahead, a second flashlight, of knowledge illuminating other points, future or past. While the Now flashlight stays steadily advancing on, the knowledge flashlight can skip back and forth on the panorama.

Another speculative possibility might be considered next. It goes beyond merely *knowing* what happened in the past or will happen in the future. It involves change. We take memory of the past for granted. On the panorama theory, there is no reason why we shouldn't have knowledge of the future of the same kind if we just knew how to achieve it. Such people as J. W. Dunne[6] and J. B. Priestly[7] interpret the panorama theory in just this way. However, once these speculations are introduced, why not introduce change? We can change present events. They're there. All the other events are there, too. So if we are unhappy about an event predicted in 2000 A.D.—that's on the panorama. We just put up a different event in that position. We change the house at 2000 A.D., and we've changed the future. Things will be different when the light of Now gets there.

That is something we take for granted. It is not quite as direct as I suggested, but the notion that the panorama is all there and could be changed suggests possibility of direct change. Instead of doing things in the present, with consequences for the future, we could influence the future directly. For that matter, there has been some discussion of the logic of changing the past. Can one not wish that something had not happened? In Orthodox-Jewish theology, I understand, it is blasphemy to pray that something not have happened in the past, because this would be a contradiction and no one can call upon God to bring about a contradiction. However, the events are all there. Why shouldn't we, for example, be able to bring it about by wishing or praying that the past should be different? I can change flag on house dated 1776. We've just changed the nature of 1776 by providing for a British victory in the Revolutionary War. We need only alter the panorama at that point.

Crawford: I am not sure about the religious significance; for instance of that change that you proposed. But I am not altogether sure that it is politically or patriotically acceptable. We are speculating at the moment.

Terrell: This was a convenient change to illustrate with no invidious political intent at all. We have suggested, in a very speculative way, the possibility of knowing the past or the future and possibility of bringing about changes in past or future. The question then arises: what about the relationship between these two speculations?

On the panorama view—as I called it—the past, the present and the future are all there. Yet, if the future is there to be known, how can it be changed?

---

[6] *An Experiment with Time* (London, 1927).

[7] *Man and Time* (London, 1964).

If you can change it, you couldn't have known it; if you can know it, you can't change it. This has led to some discussion of the relationship between knowledge of the future and fatalism. If you can *know* that something is going to happen then it seems to be beyond change; it's going to happen. We can't pursue that particular problem here.

Crawford: It would be fun to know about it all the same.

Terrell: We have to take one further possibility, though, instead of trying to change the past directly by *wishing* we might *go* there or into the future.

I have brought with me—bring it over please—a time machine. Are you familiar with the H. G. Wells' story of the time machine? As in the H. G. Wells' story, this particular machine is intended to take us as we will from this point which is Now to some other point in the past or the future. They are all there on the panorama theory of time, you see.

Hoyt: This requires an act of faith, I insist. We assume that we know about the past of which we have surviving evidence, surviving data . . .

Terrell: Which we can work with in the Now.

Bryce, are you familiar with any data about the future which we have in the Now?

Crawford: You don't have surviving evidence but you have prognosticatory evidence that different people can interpret in different ways. I think we should give this machine a test.

Beck: Before we do that, I have some reservations which I must express.

Hoyt: Go right ahead, Bob.

Beck: What happens to history? What might be the result of the experiment?

Crawford: Don't you have faith in the discussion?

Beck: I don't really know what happened. It's the first time I ever tried this trick.

Hoyt: It is very remarkable. I'll be content if you'll only provide me with some data, some evidence of the future. The historian is always dealing with the evidence that has survived from the past. Now I want evidence that comes to us from the future before I venture into the time machine; otherwise, I don't mean to express any doubts. My faith is full. Professor Terrell's remarkable time machine we know will work; nevertheless, I would feel much more confident knowing where we are going and how far we are going to the past or future.

Terrell: Would you feel more comfortable if we didn't go into the future?

Hoyt: Oh, no, I wouldn't miss this for the world. I'd love to go but I think this is a technical question that must be raised.

Crawford: I think your faith is just a little bit inadequate.

Terrell: There is this, though, on C. D. Broad's version of the panorama theory, the past was real but the future was not yet real. If he's correct, the future isn't yet there to get to. You might run into certain difficulties.

Beck: I think we should look into the future.

Crawford: I think it would be most exciting.

Hoyt: As an historian, I must confess, I would much rather go into the past.

Terrell: I am inclined to agree with Stuart. Shall we take a short trip into the past?

Beck: That's quite all right.

Terrell: A short trip. Come on gentlemen.

Crawford: Here we go. Splendid!

Terrell: Join me. After you.

Crawford: Thank you. Thank you.

[The machine is closed.]

Hoyt: It is now three seconds after one minute after 9:00 p.m.—I think. At least that's the Central Standard Time here in St. Paul; it's something else in Minneapolis. Daylight Time? In any case it is very timely that our main speaker is a professor of philosophy. Philosophy is a discipline that deals with eternal truths, according to some of the older philosophers, at least. Perhaps it could be argued that anything to do with eternal truth by definition excludes the factor of time. Surely . . .

[After a moment of confusion.]

Professor Hurwicz: This is Leo Hurwicz, alternate sponsor. I am afraid something terribly wrong must have happened with Professor Terrell's time machine. Perhaps it has been hooked up incorrectly. Whatever happened, it seems to have completely swallowed up my colleagues, Terrell, Hoyt, Beck and Crawford in time past. I feel we are just lucky that we ourselves have been returned to the present. If anyone of you have any information regarding the whereabouts of my four colleagues, I wish you would send a post card to KTCA-TV, Channel 2, Minneapolis, Minnesota 55455. However, there is one thing that I think I can assure you of. We shall have no such incidents in next week's program, which will be devoted to time and the science of men with Professor Spencer as our guest expert.

Time and the Science of Man

Anthropologists view man as a product of time over both long and short periods.

SPEAKER: *ROBERT F. SPENCER*, PROFESSOR OF ANTHROPOLOGY

COMMENTATORS: *MRS. BARBARA CUNNINGHAM*, CHAIRMAN OF THE BROOKLYN CENTER HUMAN RELATIONS COMMITTEE AND SECRETARY OF THE COMMITTEE OF CONCERN

O. MEREDITH WILSON, PRESIDENT OF THE UNIVERSITY OF MINNESOTA

Professor Hurwicz: Professor Spencer, your science has elected for itself the name anthropology, which means "the science of man." On the face of it, the name looks as though it covers all the aspects of the social activity of mankind so that other social scientists—economists, political scientists, and sociologists—might be said to form only small sections in your very vast field.

Professor Spencer: We can make that modest claim, yes.

Hurwicz: I expected some such imperialism on your part, but I am not sure we are going to put up with it without a protest. Would you indicate to us just how you limit your field?

Spencer: I have been asked whether anthropology is history. My answer is yes. I think of myself as an historian to some extent.

President Wilson: Professor Spencer, since you are an historian, perhaps you will be willing to tell us why it is that at the University we are required to maintain both a history department and an anthropology department. I may find a way to save some money.

Hurwicz: I see we are on dangerous ground after just two minutes . . . .

Spencer: We do, perhaps, make somewhat extravagant claims in that we, as anthropologists, cover a remarkable range of time. Consider, for example, the stone axe, which is the earliest evidence of man's performance. Here is one from, perhaps, a half-a-million years ago in western Europe. Examples of this kind, found across much of the Old World, indicate the time depth that we can assign to mankind. Then suddenly we make a revolutionary change. We move through time to the most extravagant kinds of development of which man is capable. Witness, for instance, the Baroque altar from the Pilgrimage Church at Vierzehneiligen in southern Germany.

The artist follows a particular style, but here he brings together the accumulated experience of literally thousands of years of human development. It is this vast panorama of man which is of interest to the anthropologist. Perhaps he differs from the historian in that he makes more grandiose claims; at least his time perspective is more all-encompassing.

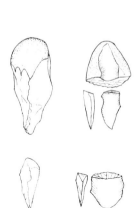

Left: Axes which were probably used in western Europe a half-a-million years ago. Drawn by Evelyn Hatcher, University graduate student in anthropology.

Right: Pilgrimage Church, 1743-72, main altar, at Vierzehnheiligen, Germany, by B. Nuemann (1687-1753).

Mrs. Cunningham: Professor Spencer, is it accurate to say that the study of anthropology deals with ancient civilizations and primitive peoples? Can we apply the premises or theories of your science to the modern day?

Spencer: You raise two questions. Anthropology is the study of ancient civilizations, yes. The archaeologist is the man with the spade who recovers the relics of the past. That can be the most ancient past, the most ancient of the Stone Ages, or the near modern past, such as the evidences of Indian life in Minnesota. This is one aspect of the field of anthropology. In this sense, anthropology is historical.

On the other hand, anthropology is broadly comparative. It is concerned with human behavior at all times and places, and attempts to compare human behavior to see whether it is possible to elicit certain principles that have significance in respect to our understanding of man as man.

Cunningham: Would it be accurate to say the study of anthropology would help us understand some of the human problems in which we are currently involved?

Spencer: I hope so. Let me present a concept or two about the ways in which the anthropologist may work with problems related to the concept of time.

Mrs. Cunningham is quite correct when she says that the anthropologist is frequently thought of as concerning himself with ancient times, with primitive man. My thesis is somewhat different. The question we have raised is whether it would be possible to look at the behavior of man living in the world today and see if the temporal concerns of the anthropologist might enable us to better understand man as man.

You may remember that shortly after World War II there was much concern with what the Japanese people were really like, also, the Germans. Today, in fact, the question is not particularly different. We are asking ourselves: What is the nature of the Russian character? What is the nature of the Red Chinese character? We want to understand them better, to see what makes them tick and why they operate as they do in the context of the modern world.

Suppose I put it to you that the time is out of joint, that we can talk about contemporary civilization or nations in terms of time and can pose certain kinds of questions relating to what time has done to man or to groups of men.

There was a great deal of attention paid to the concept of national character. I happen to be much interested in both the Germans and the Japanese. I have done some work in both countries. As an anthropologist, I am interested in explaining why the peoples of the Japanese and the German cultures react the way they do.

I should like to take one of these peoples, the Germans, and see if we cannot explain, in terms of time, why the Germans are capable on the one hand of such tremendous excellence—in the arts, in literature, in philosophy—and on the other hand, of such apparent moral degradation—genocide, the concentration camp, and all of the things which we learned to associate with the Nazi spirit.

A moment ago I suggested that the anthropologist has, perhaps, a rather broad panorama through which to view man. I also suggest that one of the concerns of the anthropologist is the human ability to invent, the ability to pile knowledge upon knowledge. I am not speaking now of evolution but of the deliberate creation of something new. It may be regarded as axiomatic that invention begets invention.

Who are the people who invent? It can be shown that they are principally the people who are at the crossroads locations of the world. Historically they are the people of the ancient Near East, living in what Breasted has called "The Fertile Crescent," the Tigris-Euphrates Valley swinging over to the Nile Valley; in the river systems of India, such as the Ganges and the Indus; or in the river systems of China, as in the Yellow River Valley. Middle America might be considered another such area because our American Indian certainly was one of the founders of a great civilization.

We certainly can trace our own beginnings back to the confluence of ideas that arose in the Fertile Crescent. We are the direct heirs of the ancient peoples, the ancient Semites and the Egyptians. We see, however, that centers shift, that there can be changes, that from the ancient world of the Near East there was a swing to Greece, to Rome, and so ultimately to Europe. In other words, human activity doesn't remain static either in time or in place. It shifts geographically just as it shifts in time.

What is indicated here is that man is the product of what has gone before. He is the product of time. He draws from the accumulated experience of the generations which have preceded him. Since no culture, no human system remains static, there is a constant state of flux. Man changes through time. However, if there is isolation, if man is spatially away from such crossroads, then he might be said to occupy a kind of marginal position. Away from the centers of development, this marginal position can be one of stagnation, one of limited achievement. Furthermore, it can result in a situation of imbalance in the social system.

A social system may be seen as a kind of organism, a whole made up of different parts. The concept is simple enough. Religion, economic life, social and family life are parts which dovetail, hanging together in precise and definable ways. As culture changes, the constellation of the parts changes as well, and the end result is that periods of balance and periods of imbalance arise.

In the German situation, there is a kind of paradox—a culture which produces both excellence and excess. The Germans are a Western people who share in the same civilization as we do, or as the British or French, but they are a Western people who were caught in a marginal-geographical and marginal-temporal situation and whose behavior thus might be appraised in a somewhat different way than that of the others. An imbalance arising through the vagaries of time becomes characteristic.

Before us, then, is the idea of a whole culture and the concept of a national culture or a national character. When, after World War II, attempts were made to perceive the German national character and to evaluate it, much attention was paid to the genetic, to the racial background. Obviously, this is dangerous. There was also much attention paid to psychoanalytic or psychiatric characterizations. It was said that the Germans behaved in the excessive way they did simply because they had stern fathers, that they were cowed as children, and so took out their patterns of vengeance against the rest of the world simply because of this suppression by an authoritarian figure. Adolph Hitler was, himself, an authoritarian figure reflecting the same pattern.

This is interesting but, really, not very convincing. On the other side of the coin, there is the picture of the German ideal family, the benign German father and the happy balance in family relations. This psychiatric, psychoanalytic explanation goes too far and fails to offer an adequate explanation. We are confronted with the fact of German excellence and of German excess.

It should be stressed that the Germans are chosen here simply because they seem to offer a case for the argument of time influencing man. I could have just as readily chosen the Japanese, offering a parallel case, and, certainly, one could consider the Soviet Union today. The Russians provide an equally good example.

To make the concept of marginality and cultural development meaningful, one has to look at the panorama of history. The map serves to indicate how temporal and spatial relationships affect the development of the German character. Note what has happened. There are the Italians, the Spanish, the French, the Germans. Forgetting exact political boundaries, it can be seen that each ethnic entity in Europe occupies its special place.

Admittedly, it is a little difficult to say precisely what Germans are. They are certainly not a race. They don't necessarily have a single language. In fact, until 1870 they were not even a single, unified nation. They were always a whole series of petty little states. It has never been really difficult to differentiate the man from Hamburg from the Bavarian or the Hessians from the Westphalians. Clearly, the Austrians stand out rather distinctly, yet they, too, might also fall into the German pattern. Differences, not similarities, seem to stand out.

In the ancient Near East—Egypt and Babylonia—there was a focal center of growth. Then a shift to the Hellenistic area took place, to the Grecian peninsula where new ideas, new thoughts seem to have been generated, again as the result of contact between peoples. Witness, for instance, the rise of Alexander, the meaning of the Alexandrian campaigns, and the spreading of Hellenism through-

out the ancient world. There was then a shift to Rome with the ascendancy of the Roman empire.

Then came a long period of darkness, the Dark Ages in Europe, a cultural stasis. In that medieval world of Europe, our own ancestry lay in stagnation. It was a time when integration of the elements composing the societies of Europe was imperfectly achieved. The medieval stereotype recalls to mind the castle and men going about in iron clothes. Perhaps there was a little attention paid to learning, but learning was in Latin and Latinity seems to have imposed a uniform badge across medieval Europe.

Then something happened—the re-awakening of and an awareness of the East. The rise of the Crusades, the emergence of Aquinas and others. They were factors of change. We are discussing a matter which may be seen in the somewhat broader terms of the culture of the area. The Crusades were instrumental in spreading Levantine culture, and an awareness of it, into Italy.

Later on, the discovery of America brought in the wealth of the Americas and created in western Europe that kind of crossroads situation to which reference has already been made. The Italian Renaissance marked the beginning of modern times. It introduced a new spirit in Europe. As a result of the introduction of that new spirit into Europe, there came the rise of imperial Spain; in France, increasing social and political self-awareness, the period of Francis I and the Golden Age of Louis XIV; in England there came the Age of Consolidation under Henry VII, the strength of the period of Henry VIII, and the vital age of Elizabeth I. What is suggested here? In Italy, Spain, France, and Britain, a series of what can be called integrated cultures emerged, cultures marked by energetic creativity.

As an example, what is characteristic of the period of Elizabeth I? Shakespeare is present in the latter part of the Elizabethan reign, but there are also a great many other creative and significant writers. There is an interest in Flemish painting and development of an English musical style. There is the beginning of a systematic philosophy in the work of Francis Bacon, who became the first significant philosopher of modern times. There are parallels in France, certainly in Spain also, and one can look at the Italian peninsula and see much the same process in operation there. Excellence was achieved in the arts, to thought, to music, to what generally might be called the humanities. Also, there was an integrated society that is in a state of balance. Men were free. Men were able to achieve the ability for self-expression and creative vitality.

What has happened in Germany? The Germans, like the Russians, were away from the mainstream of Europe. The Alps stood between. France, a linguistic entity, separated from the Germans. The Russians were far away. Scandinavia, of course, was very much removed. If productivity, inventiveness, and creativity are characteristic of those areas of Europe which become focal for the broad period in question, Germany remained marginal. I have suggested that as a factor of marginality, extremes and excesses arise.

One might say that Martin Luther, who died in 1546, really typifies the Renaissance spirit. He clearly does, but he also represents something of an extremist point of view in his break with tradition. He was no longer part of a whole; he was moving off on a kind of tangent. What Martin Luther—or for that matter Calvin, or John Huss, or other similar figures of the period—seemed to exemplify is the imperfection of integration and the fact that the parts of the total society do not dovetail in quite the same way as in the crossroads countries. There was, as a result, a certain kind of extreme dimension injected into the *Zeitgeist* of the culture. Isn't it curious that as the Elizabethan Age progressed— as the age of Louis XIV developed, or that of Charles V in Spain, or as the petty principalities of Italy fought their wars which nonetheless contributed a great deal to the world of the time—yet Germany should hang far behind? Isn't it curious that in the period immediately after Luther there is really nothing in literature that is worthy of the name? My colleagues in the German department may object to this, but I believe that in terms of demonstrable achievement, in terms of an effect on the pages of world history, this is well indicated. It was not until quite some time later that Germany began to come into its own. Only long after Luther, when Lutheranism and the Reformation had been integrated, did we begin to get a new spurt in Germany.

What has been happening in the rest of Europe all this time? One may think of such prominent creative figures as Hobbes, Locke, and Hume; of Descartes or Condorcet in France; of such Spanish literary figures as Cervantes, and much earlier, of Dante, in Italy, and a host of others. Are there any parallels in Germany? There have not been any yet except for Luther.

Not until the eighteenth century, the Age of Enlightenment, did Germany move into its own. Then, of course, came the great literary age, the threshold of the great musical age, and of the great philosophical age. This eighteenth century German growth is the time of Goethe, of Lessing, of Schiller, of Klopstock, the great figures of German literature. How much later they are than Shakespeare! How much later than Racine or Moliere! This delay suggests that Germany had marginal development which occurred relatively late in time.

When a marginal development occurs, there is a tendency to move to extremes. Nowhere in Europe do we get the same impact of—say—literature as in the development of the German Romantic movement at the end of the eighteenth century. Consider, too, how much later this developed in the Russian context. Again, Immanuel Kant poses a series of problems which the Germans have really never resolved and which the nineteenth century saw them attempt to resolve again and again.

The problem over which the Germans agonized was that of a rigid social system as against the concept of freedom of will. It is no accident that our concept of academic freedom—freedom on the part of both the instructor and the student—is one that developed in Germany. The attempt to deal with human freedom is certainly a part of the German context. Yet there was the imbalance that the social system militated against the expression of such freedoms. It can be argued that the same thing happened under Marxism. It is no accident that Marx is a German. Clearly, the issue of authority and freedom has no more been resolved by Communism than it was in nineteenth century Germany. These together form a paradox. This paradox is characteristic of German culture.

Admittedly, I have considered a vast expanse of history in a very short period of time. Perhaps, however, without violating the facts of history, the argument of German temporal marginality has some substance. I have suggested that by understanding time in relation to the sequence of development in space, we can understand why a people acts as it does, behaves as it does, and may through imbalance contribute such excellence on one hand and excess on the other.[1]

Hurwicz: Professor Spencer, you have indeed covered a great deal of ground. I think it is quite natural for us to want to question some of the conclusions. I think it would be good to start out by making sure that we understand the exact nature of your analytical framework. In particular, one thing occurred to me. I have a book published about 1950, by a Frenchman, Andre Siegfried. The title of his book indicates what I have in mind, *Nations Have Souls*. I'll read the beginning to give you an opportunity to indicate whether this is similar to your point of view:

> There is a psychology of all people, a certain fundamental base that makes itself constantly felt. In many of our traits we resemble the Gauls, who were our ancestors, and the characteristics noted by Tacitus in the Barbarians are still recognizable in the Germans . . .[2]

You see, there is an adherent personality of a people that goes, at least, 2,500 years back. Someone might think that when you talk about why Germans are like this or like that, you have a similar view of this phenomenon.

---

[1] The thesis presented here is expounded at greater length in "The German Paradox: A Study in National Character," *Journal of the Minnesota Academy of Science*, Vol. 32, no. 3, August, 1965.

[2] p. 3.

I should hope I haven't given that impression, because I am really looking at a series of ideas drawn from different times and places which have been put together in a particular way. They come about not because of any soul, so to speak, not because of any hidden abstruse psychic propensity on the part of people, but simply through the actions of the historic process.

Wilson: Dr. Spencer, I am a little intrigued by the fact that it is Andre Siegfried whom Dr. Hurwicz has called to our attention. It reminds me of the fact that he also undertook to write about the United States in a book called *Les Etats Unis.* I am sure if Dr. Siegfried were here, he would say that the United States is much more marginal than Germany. Indeed, it brings me to call attention to your map because there is something a little troublesome about your definition of marginality if, for instance, the heart countries are Italy and Spain. The Near Eastern mathematics was pumped into Spain, and Near Eastern philosophy was sometimes pumped into Italy. As a matter of fact, any place that was away from the Near East was marginal.

Spencer: It was marginal at that time.

Wilson: Yes. Certainly in that period England would have been thought of as more marginal than Germany. Any simple view of the map would make England at least as marginal as Germany. There is another view of the reason for the difference in the output of German culture which emphasizes the time factor of your program more than the geographical marginality.

Dr. Schmidt, who was head of the Kriegsgeschickte seminar in Heidelberg, Germany, would have said—and did say, as a matter of fact—that France had a clear reason for centrality and a heart culture. This was because the Rhone, the Loire and the Seine all arose in an area near Paris so that all one had to do was to follow one of these three rivers and he would come to the core of the country from any part of the frontier. England had a natural reason for unity because she was an island and did not have any other place to go. Germany was all split up into many nations and fought herself to death over culture mostly because her rivers crossed the country in widely separated parallel valleys instead of arising in a common highland. The Elbe, for example, and the Rhine had neither a common origin nor a common mouth and led the people away from each other instead of into some kind of communion.

Spencer: I'm not prepared to deny this. However, we are confronted with a problem, one I can only allude to in passing. What is a nation? What are people who constitute a nation? What are the Germans, for example? One can't define them in racial terms. One can perhaps define them broadly in geographic terms, but one cannot even define them in linguistic terms. Hence, it would seem that the Germans represent a particular geographic-historic focus that reflects marginality at a given point in time and a continuing imperfection, as I have called it, or imbalance in the way in which the parts are put together. Some features, as I have suggested, are out of joint. This, I believe, is not true of France and not of Spain in the sixteenth century, although it might well be true of Spain today.

I was interested in your earlier statement regarding Siegfried, who would regard, as you say, the United States as infinitely more marginal than Germany ever could be.

Wilson: There is no question about it. As a matter of fact, his book tries to explain the United States to Americans. He predicts that although the United States is Protestant and has been greatly influenced by western Europe, the nation will emerge as Catholic and will be more affected by eastern Europe, and that it will continue to remain marginal in a geographic sense. Moreover, we will have conflicts of cultures internally which will postpone the day when anybody will read an American book—a common epithet of the nineteenth century which is still believed in much of France today.

Cunningham: This talk about marginal countries has been interesting to me. Europe is geographically smaller than the United States. Would the United States be considered a marginal society of Europe, for example, or could it be a total society with marginal societies of its own?

Spencer: I do think that, perhaps, the concept of modern industrialization, of rapidity of communication, does change the picture a bit. My argument has been that we have focal centers and we have margins. I suppose the figure would be like the ripples which go out from a stone which is dropped into a puddle; the further out they go, the less pronounced they become. If the United States, according to Siegfried, is marginal, then what is the center today?

Hurwicz: Some people talk about the "polycentric" era that we live in. Perhaps that's the answer.

Wilson: I think the answer to the question you asked, Mrs. Cunningham, was implicit in the illustration. Andre Siegfried, who wrote the book, is a Frenchman— and so the center is clear. He and Mr. de Gaulle had the same long nose, their culture.

Hurwicz: Of course, we should be a little careful. If we were saying that the United States were the center and we were claiming that it was France, I think the theories would deserve more attention. However, if we respectively see ourselves as centers, this is a geocentric kind of approach that is under suspicion even if it happens to be correct.

Cunningham: I should think that the United States is a peculiar illustration because we don't have a geographic center of culture. It would seem to me that our crossroads would be found on both coasts. We have a nation on either side of us—to the north and to the south—yet we affect them very little, I would think. So the question of a marginal society would have to be considered within our own boundaries. Consider the Indian, the Negro both north and south, and the white Southerner. Southerners strongly emphasize the Southern way of life; they feel that it is a separate culture. I would hope that the kind of thing that you study and the kind of explanations you find would help some of us to deal more effectively with the white Southerner.

Spencer: I suggested that we are looking at a concept of national character. For instance, there are Germans; there are Frenchmen; there are Americans. Now, admittedly, I am not altogether on safe ground here because there are any number of my fellow social scientists who would say that this concept of national character is the grossest charlantry, and that, really, we can't accurately elicit it. They feel that the concept fails to recognize the tremendous range of differences such as may be suggested for the United States. Yet, I am not altogether convinced that this is true. I think that anyone who has had the experience of passing across the Canadian border is aware of something that reflects a difference between the American of the United States and the American of Canada. One has only to pass across the boundary from Germany into Austria to be aware of an entirely different—shall I call it "spirit"? I'm troubled by this as everyone must be in an age when we like to pin these things down with exact precision.

Wilson: Professor Spencer, I would like to turn to Professor Hurwicz's comment of a moment ago. Remember, he said that there would be a great deal more significance to this discussion if America were describing itself as marginal to France and the Frenchman describing France as marginal to the United States. Mrs. Cunningham asked "Where is the center of the United States?" Immediately I realized the fact that the New Yorker is quite sure where the center is. I'm sure the person in Washington, D.C. is quite sure where the center is. Maybe we are back to Dr. Hurwicz's suggestion that what would be significant would be breaking the egocentric or the ethnocentric barriers when we are talking about marginality.

Spencer: Yes, that's true. I feel it necessary to raise a word of caution here, however. I do think that one can define a center with a certain amount of exactness, purely statistically, for example, in terms of the kinds of achievements that the locus can demonstrate.

Hurwicz: Let me, for a moment, go back to see whether we accept the rationale of this theory as distinct from whether we are in agreement with a particular application of it.

It is a quite reasonable idea that if you are in a center where things are developing, you could expect to find certain phenomena occurring there which you wouldn't expect in the provinces. It is quite possible that the center for the live stage is in New York and the center for the movies is Hollywood. I would have no objections to stressing the impact of the center of development. For instance, I imagine that if you went back to the stone axe era, to the African Olduvai Gorge where they were producing thousands of stone axes, you would find people coming in from hundreds of miles to find out how axe-making was done. They would be very much impressed by the local industry and sophistication. Yet when we try to correlate this with what you refer to as excesses, then I find it a little more difficult to correlate the extent to which a certain point could be described as a crossroads and the extent to which it engaged in excesses.

Let me give just one example. Perhaps it is unfair, but I was trying to think who in antiquity had something of a reputation for genocide. I think the Assyrians did very well. The Assyrians happened to have been in the Fertile Crescent. They did, as you indicated, have several outstanding things in the field of culture, art, commerce, mathematics, astrology, and so forth. I think, in many ways, they were very balanced if you look at what they were doing internally. At the same time, they did terrible things. In fact, they tried to exterminate the rest of the Fertile Crescent.

Spencer: I'm not so sure about that. They moved the others around.

Hurwicz: They moved some of them around. Those who wouldn't let themselves be moved around . . .

Wilson: Isn't it true that even the moving around was a form of extinction? They were trying to destroy the culture which, in a sense, is as serious as destroying the person.

Cunningham: What I remember about the Assyrian is that he came down like a wolf on the fold.

Hurwicz: Of course, this is a biased report.

Wilson: That raises another question about the wolf. I was fascinated by your discussion of Germans and your use of Luther as an example. As an historian, I am troubled that we don't take into consideration the fact that Luther, while raising a tremendous idea, was quite literary and perhaps potentially the forerunner of both poetic and artistic development. However, he happened to deal with a subject of intense personal concern, one involved with emotions and prejudices, or faith; one that contains all of the seeds of human anguish and suffering. Both love and hate were bound up in the questions he asked, with the result that what flowed from his essays was an immediate and tremendous psychological and cultural conflict which didn't subside until after the Thirty Years War.

The Thirty Years War, if I remember correctly, wiped out about two-thirds of the population of the Rhine Valley. There wasn't enough energy left to provide more than the means to national recovery. The issue could really be the question of whether the misfortune of Germany was, not that Germany was marginal, but that the man who was Germany's first literary light raised a question so explosive they weren't able, really, to deal with it in a rational way.

Spencer: I can turn that around, though, and ask whether it would have been possible for so explosive a question to have been raised except in the context of an imbalanced social system.

Wilson: Well, I could answer that. The question was raised constantly, and the only reason the British solution was different was that Henry VIII had the channel between him and the Papal countries. He was more marginal than the rest and he could, therefore, develop a local Protestant church that didn't get involved or engulfed in the same violence. Because of these facts, he could have a Church of England.

Spencer: One tends to be drawn—as Professor Hurwicz says—into the loci of productivity, saying that here art is produced, here music is produced, here thought is produced. This is not really what I mean. I am tinking of the totality of production. Luther to me represents a great man, perhaps ahead of his time, out of his time, operating with influences which are transalpine, which come to him out of the spirit of the Renaissance.

But yet, the whole spirit of the time doesn't seem to be right for the reception of the Lutheran idea. Parallel things which could be giving him support are not happening when Luther brings forth his concepts of salvation by faith. Your objection, Dr. Wilson, is well taken, I think, in that he so upsets the time that this precludes the development of other portions of the culture. Nevertheless, I am less happy with such an explanation because it places the burden on an individual and fails to come to grips with culture and historical processes.

Wilson: Let's try one other approach, then. There is, at least in the German mind, a parallel productivity in art. You and I can say that Albrecht Dürer is an artist. We certainly can't say that he is not a great artist. It can be that the severity, the mascularity, the pain of an Albrecht Dürer etching or painting reflects the terrible psychological, emotional, or cultural tensions of the Germans. Certainly, there isn't anything greater in art that I know of in England at that time, and Dürer and Grünewald were of approximately the same period as the Italian Renaissance artists you describe as central. I suspect if I knew more about music I could even find a musician or two with which to trouble you.

Spencer: I choose to take refuge in my social science integration of the parts dovetailing to form the whole. The thing that seems to me so characteristic of England in the period of Henry, perhaps more precisely of Elizabeth, is this whole question of freedom in social structure, plasticity of society. These products —however great they may be—are still mere products. It is rather the climate out of which they come that is the revealing thing, not the products themselves.

Hurwicz: I wonder whether we might return, for a moment, to the question that Mrs. Cunningham raised, namely, the relationship of these ideas and their implications, if we were to accept them. Would they help us analyze present-day phenomena in the United States?

Cunningham: Can they help to analyze, specifically, the emergence of a present-day Martin Luther and the kind of society for which he speaks and the kind of idea that he presents?

Spencer: You mean Martin Luther King?

Cunningham: Yes.

Spencer: Actually, I tend to look at this in a little different way in that I do feel there is an American national character that is different from Canadian national character, of British, or French, or others. Our ways of solving problems are rather well fixed for us by custom, tradition, religion, value systems, and law, so that even if we diverge in behavior, we are still conforming to a pattern that is quite distinctly our own.

Wilson: I find myself in full agreement with you, but reluctant—perhaps, by lack of familiarity—to accept all the explanations. I think we have a national character, too. Anthropologists have not yet said very well what it is or how it expresses itself. Yet, we don't really hide the fact when we go to another country. We are identified as Americans and whatever our differences are, they are recognized when we are abroad.

I can think of a balancing explanation which I'd like an anthropologist to test. Because I am a chauvinistic historian, I am prepared to guess that the rate of developing nationalism better explains the flowering of German culture than does the concept of marginality. There were features internal to Germany, including the geographic features referred to, which were such sources of conflict that nationalism could not emerge, and the people did not achieve either national identification or peace of mind. Nor did they win a measure of time which would permit intellectual or artistic development in quite the same way as in France or England.

Spencer: I can answer that German nationalism doesn't come until 1870 or shortly before with the rise of Prussian nationalism; this in itself is reflective of marginal lateness.

Wilson: It reflects lateness, yes, but the marginal concept keeps troubling me. I think it could be bound up with the fact that rivers flowed the wrong way or that the north and the south were divided on the problem of religion. There were a variety of things that kept them apart.

Spencer: Still, I like your nationalist hypothesis. We could set up a nationalism of Scandinavia under the kings of Sweden. Certainly under Charles XII and in parallel periods there was great expansion. However, there is no compensating spirit of nationalism. There is no sense of Scandinavian nationalism. It is still a local nationalism. It's Danish, Norwegian, Swedish, or Finnish nationalism. We see the end product of this today.

Hurwicz: This question has already been raised, but in a slightly different way. Suppose this kind of analysis had been attempted in about 1840. Of course people would agree that the Germans are different from the French, and the French from the Italians, and so on, but would there, at that time, have been the feeling that the Germans were so unique, that they had the potential for such extremes in both directions? You see, I think at that time people had fresh in their minds the extremes of the French Revolution and of Napoleon. Some of them talked about Napoleon in the way we talk about recent German events. You were talking about chauvinism or ethnocentrism of nations. Now, I wonder about the temporal aspect. Is our perspective sound?

Spencer: Yes, I think it is. I think that you are quite right in respect to the concepts of the French Revolution, but consider what had happened. The Revolution was an end product of the Age of Enlightenment of the eighteenth century, but it represents a kind of sudden collapse, a shift away from centrality, so to speak.

Hurwicz: We have come to the point where we don't have much of an opportunity for a detailed discussion. Would you give us some sort of concise wrap-up of the way you see this problem. It would be helpful since we have been tearing about in a variety of directions.

Spencer: Very briefly, it is simply this. When men come together, ideas are born; when ideas are born there is a certain energy that is generated. There are, then, points of focal energy, of inventiveness, and there are points that are removed from such centers. Where there are points removed from the centers, namely, marginal areas, the absence of inventiveness also makes for ideas coming in at disparate times, which means that they are put together differently and that the end result is frequently disjointed. This is why I said that time was out of joint.

Time and Space in Baroque Architecture

Do you go for Baroque?

SPEAKER: *HYLTON A. THOMAS*, PROFESSOR OF ART

COMMENTATORS: *WALTER W. HELLER*, PROFESSOR OF ECONOMICS AND FORMER CHAIRMAN OF THE PRESIDENT'S COUNCIL OF ECONOMIC ADVISORS

    LESLIE MacFARLANE, VISITING PROFESSOR OF HISTORY AT MACALESTER COLLEGE

Professor Hoyt: Historians, considering the long sweep of the past and noting that there are changes constantly taking place, divide up the totality of the past into periods. These succeeding periods are often characterized by particular features that are especially distinctive in the sphere of cultural history, and, within cultural history, the history of art. There are other periods to which historians have given the label of "neo-this" or "pseudo-that," indicating a revival of the period which bears the original label. As a pendulum moves from one end of its swing to the other, cultural history seems to move between periods labeled rationalistic and romantic. We are dealing with one of those periods tonight, the romantic episode of the Baroque.

We have an excellent example in the Twin Cities—right in our midst—of a neo-Baroque structure. Hylton, would you begin this evening by commenting on the Cathedral of St. Paul, which is a good example of a revival of a past period of architectural style.

Professor Thomas: It is, in a sense, Baroque, although more properly, as you said, neo-Baroque. It's a structure which has many of the qualities that fine Baroque architecture had. As far as I am concerned, unfortunately, it is not a really great example of Baroque architecture.

Professor Heller: Do you mean really great in terms of contemporary Baroque or in terms of historical Baroque?

Thomas: I mean in terms of fine Baroque, which, for example, is large and powerful. The Cathedral happens to be well-sited, which is often one of the splendid characteristics of very fine Baroque architecture, but unfortunately the architect was not a first-rate architect and the building is, perhaps, not a first-rate building.

Heller: Is it possible that this is an expression of mid-twentieth-century judgment and that a hundred years from now this might, in terms of other peoples' values, be considered a very wonderful example?

The St. Paul Cathedral sits on the brow of Summit Hill overlooking the city of St. Paul. Finished in 1915, it took nearly ten years to build.

Thomas: That's possible, but only because with time, attitudes change to some extent. Many of us, for example, thought 20 or 30 years ago that Victorian architecture was often really deplorable. Subsequently it has picked up a certain amount of charm. One certainly can often extract some pleasure from it now.

Heller: We are retreating just a little bit too fast here. It seems to me that there must be some standards of what's good in Baroque architecture, and that these must be widely accepted. If this isn't good Baroque architecture, why should it become good in 30 years?

Professor MacFarlane: Are we starting at the beginning? Couldn't you tell us how Baroque arose?

Thomas: Yes, I can, very briefly.

Baroque started in Rome in about 1600. It is the first true post-classical Roman architectural style. There are certain obvious reasons for it. One is the relatively stable religious condition. In most of Europe by about 1600, the Counter-Reformation had been successful, at least according to the Roman Catholic Church, and the Church was fairly well re-established in the Mediterranean area, Austria,

Piazza e Basilica di San Pietro.

Bavaria, France, and Flanders. The Papal States were free from trouble and Rome was increasingly becoming important and wealthy. There were many great papal families continuously embellishing Rome as the religious capital of western Europe and as a great and almost imperial city.

MacFarlane: Yes. Wasn't it a Borghese who built part of St. Peter's?

Thomas: Yes, and I am afraid his name was displayed very prominently across the entablature of the façade.

MacFarlane: Of course, there was also their family palace, the Borghese Palace.

Thomas: As a matter of fact, Baroque Rome was not only a religious center, but a secular center of Europe. The great families embellished it with family palaces, churches, chapels, and monuments. Monuments were both secular and funerary. Fountains like the great fountain called that of Paul the Fifth were practical because Rome needed more water. This fountain was also an expression of this new sense of self-confidence, of power that has come. It was made, it seems, to be something close to arrogant. You see how forthright and domineering, or at least dominating, a great piece of secular Baroque architecture it is.

Fountain of Paul V by Carlo Maderna (1556-1629).

Heller: Was most of this Baroque architecture you just mentioned secular? Of course, there was church Baroque, but wasn't there a new class—I am looking at it now as an economist—a ruling class of rich merchants coming into being? Didn't they commission such works?

Thomas: Sometimes they did. The Chigi family had established itself in banking in Rome in the sixteenth century. By the seventeenth century there was a Chigi Pope; they were already a great Roman semi-papal family. Some of the other families came into great prominence only after a member of the family became pope.

Hoyt: Is this necessarily relevant to the origins of Baroque as a style?

Heller: Was the artist necessarily relevant to the origins of Baroque as a style?

Thomas: Essentially yes. Most of these merchants came along and took up what the artist told them was good art.

The Baroque is largely a new style; it has its roots in the near past. It continues certain qualities that the later sixteenth century had already developed—certain church plans, for example, and certain palace types. It takes over certain fanciful aspects of later sixteenth-century architecture, and also reacts against the rather mannered style of that period. It goes back to the High Renaissance for bigness, solidity, and power. Undoubtedly, since it is a Roman style, the great monuments of antiquity, like the Colosseum for example, have had some effect. Some of the major High Renaissance structures like the Palazzo Farnese obviously have been influenced by the grandeur of ancient Rome.

Heller: These have struck me as being heavy and static.

Thomas: There are obviously changes, of course, between Renaissance and Baroque. It could not be only a continuation of the Renaissance. Quite clearly, one of the most essential characteristics of the Baroque style is architectural movement, which I hope to define in a moment.

Heller: Before you go on with the architectural part of it, what's the relationship of Baroque architecture to the decorative arts, as compared with Renaissance and Gothic for example?

Thomas: One can find comparable qualities. One speaks of Baroque music and the Baroque in painting.

Heller: What I was trying to get at is that in the Gothic period, architecture really predominates and everything else is subordinate to it. In the Renaissance there was a greater equality among the arts of sculpture, painting, and architecture. What about Baroque architecture? What is its relationship to painting, sculpture, and so on? Are they coordinate or subordinate?

Thomas: As a matter of fact, in the best examples, a kind of unity exists where architecture and sculpture, painting, and the so-called decorative arts have been fused.

Heller: This is what I was trying to get at. In what respect do you regard that part as the reflection of the times? I have read that a type of architecture is a matter of the mind, the spirit of the times. Why is this? Where does this unity come from? How does it affect the social, the political, the economic structure of the times?

Thomas: Frankly, I can't answer that conclusively. One doesn't always know exactly why a style develops in a certain way.

MacFarlane: It seems to be a gradual style. I am thinking of the Capitoline Hill, the beautiful thing that Michelangelo did where there are very graceful steps leading into the Piazza with various views of all the buildings at different angles. This seems to be Baroque, Roman Baroque, rather than Renaissance. Certainly, it formerly had a heavy, flat façade. Now the artist is working with light and shade and with angles—the trees against the sky moving against the background of the Capitoline Hill, the stairway graced with lovely views, and so on. This seems to be the best and earliest kind of Baroque.

Thomas: This certainly gets us to Michelangelo, one of the great sources for Baroque style as it comes into being. His use of angles was one of the foundations for the new style; the diagonal was important in Baroque architecture. It wasn't absolutely new, but I don't know whether I could say that I know exactly why all the characteristics tended to fuse in this particular movement in architecture.

Heller: I am really glad for such an honest answer, because I get so—what shall I say—dubious sometimes when I am told that Gothic can only have happened in this age and Baroque could only have happened in that age. Perhaps you are not denying that, but I have difficulty assuming that only a particular architecture could develop out of the economic and social and political and religious conditions in a particular period.

Hoyt: A form of literature or a style of art can have within it its own means of development and much of that development is predictable from what has already been developed in the early stages of a particular style of art. Most historians will answer Walter's question by saying that you started out with an unproved premise, that art must reflect something. It might be reflecting itself, that is, reflecting the artists' development of a style within their own minds.

Thomas: It certainly can reflect a great deal on the personality of the artist, of Michelangelo, for example.

MacFarlane: I am thinking of the Jesuits, or the Society of Jesus. After the Counter-Reformation, they were able to go ahead with their doctrines and one of the dominant themes was preaching. They had to have a wide nave, a nave which was uncluttered by columns so that they could see their congregation and the congregation could hear them. Therefore the nave was made wide and flat and the side aisles were usually relegated to the flanking chapels.

Thomas: In other words, you mean to say that functionalism is not a twentieth-century phenomenon!

Heller: We have mentioned briefly several of the common features of Baroque art, and particularly, architecture. Could you spell out in a little more detail the elements of bigness or monumentality, the great size for which Baroque architects strove.

Thomas: Certainly. Let's look at the Piazza Navona in Rome, which involves two of the great architects of the seventeenth century: Bernini and Borromini. In the first place, this was built on what had survived of the Circus of Domitian, which was a very large imperial Roman structure, and which gives the reason for this long narrow shape with its curving end. It also became the headquarters for the family of a new pope, the Pamfili family, who built the Pamfili palace, the church, and this great fountain, which was a major ornament for the area. Secondary palaces built by people related to the Pamfili suddenly turned the area into a great Baroque complex. A large part of its impressiveness is simply a result

Piazza Navona in Rome by Francesco Borromini (1599-1677) and Bernini (1598-1680).

of its great size, its enormous sweep, and of the very dominant accent of this great fountain by Bernini in the center.

Again, if one looks at something by Maderna and Rainaldi, for example, Sant' Andrea, one of the biggest of the Roman Baroque churches, one can see that its height and breadth have both been exaggerated slightly to make one of the biggest of the Roman Baroque churches appear even bigger and to make it, in fact, a dominant architectural note in a very big city. These Baroque structures were meant to announce themselves.

MacFarlane: I must confess I find this one of the most disturbing features of the Baroque—its vulgarity, its ostentatiousness.

Thomas: It is self-assertive. It is an expression of an age having great confidence in itself and which had no shame in announcing this. We have already said that Pope Paul V had his name spelled across the façade of Saint Peter's.

Heller: I would call that decidedly vulgar. In the same way, the Foshay Tower has "Foshay" written across the tower.

MacFarlane: In addition, it is false. As you see, Sant' Andrea has an enormous façade. Well, this is almost a false façade.

111

Sant'Andrea della Vallee by Maderna and Rainaldi, started in 1624.

Thomas: It is not really false. It is expanded, but it is expanded deliberately to make, in a sense, the greatness of the church emphatically visible to the audience.

Hoyt: If you live with a style of art, you have a different viewpoint from that which you get from simply studying photographic examples of the style. Professor MacFarlane, you spent many years in Rome and you had to live with these things. How has that influenced your judgment?

MacFarlane: It's true I have lived two years in Rome. I was a student for two years in Rome and came home only for vacations. These buildings do impress one. You unconsciously absorb them, the enormousness of them, and of Rome. It's one of the most exciting cities of the world. I do love it and I think every time one goes back there, he gets a thrill and an excitement of anticipation that he never gets in any other city in the world. At the same time, I still think it's ostentatious. It presses in on you.

Thomas: It's meant to dominate and to be an almost overpowering expression of the new power, the new ease, the greatness of Rome.

Heller: I hope this is not the wrong place to ask this question. You say "this greatness of Rome." I am rather in the dark; I gather it shows primarily Rome because it is a Roman creation.

Thomas: It is a Roman creation.

Heller: Again, I am interested in the spread of the Baroque through Europe, both its area dimensions and its time dimensions. Did it spread more quickly than some of the preceding styles because of the invention of the printing press?

Thomas: To a certain extent it did.

Heller: Then, did it maintain the same form, this overpowering nature?

Thomas: Not invariable. There is great variety of shape in examples of Baroque architecture. This is less true in France than in Italy, and almost more so in Germany and Austria in the eighteenth century.

MacFarlane: I think you can tell the difference between Austrian Baroque, German Baroque, and Roman. When I was in Innsbruck a few years ago, I was charmed by the Amalienburg Chapel because of its delicacy.

Heller: You are speaking of the Baroque per se, not the Rococo?

MacFarlane: No, I mean the Baroque—for instance, Maximilian's chapel and his tomb.

Thomas: It is also true that, in Germany especially, the troubled conditions delayed the appearance of the Baroque until the last part of the seventeenth century. Of course, what you have is really a kind of Renaissance.

Heller: How about France? How fast did it develop there? You said about 1600 in Italy. Did it spread to France then?

Thomas: France was also slow in its adaptation of the full Baroque. First it developed a definition of kingship and then began to express this architecturally under Louis XIV at Versailles about 1675.

MacFarlane: This is something that has puzzled me. Why did the French never find the sacred building, the church, as successful in the Baroque? Was the domestic architecture potentially more interested in the Baroque forms?

Thomas: Well, this is because the church had already become subservient to the state.

MacFarlane: I see; the state dominated the church.

Thomas: However, it is true that one of the more important qualities of Baroque and of great Roman Baroque was the enormous variety of form, of structure, of shape. Look at another great church, the Santa Maria in Capitelli by Rainaldi. Rainaldi did very odd things from the Renaissance point of view, but kept certain Renaissance elements, like the classical orders. He would pull out the columns, or double and triple them, or increase moldings, so that the structure

Santa Maria in Capitelli by Carlo Rainaldi (1611-1691).

ended with an extremely dramatic façade which can move in and out, backwards and forwards, with a very strong play of light and shade. The façade becomes almost as much like sculpture as like architecture.

MacFarlane: I think this is dishonest. I don't think you can play around with stone. Stone is very heavy.

Thomas: Nevertheless, it is fun to play around with.

MacFarlane: Well, it might be fun. It has interesting light and shade, but I I think you ought not do this with stone.

Thomas: Then let's look at it from the Renaissance point of view. The church of Santa Maria della Consolazione at Todi is a perfect Renaissance building. It is very clear, very simple; the interior space is expressed by the exterior; horizontals and verticals are nicely balanced.

Chiesa di Santa Maria della Consolazione, XVI secolo, in Todi, Italy, by Cola di Caprarola.

MacFarlane: Is that what you mean by honesty?

Thomas: Yes.

MacFarlane: There are no frills, nothing unnecessary. You see, this is what disturbs me about Baroque. A genuine architectural form must be formed organically in growth from within. Stone will do this, whereas the Roman Baroque church, with its plaster work and stucco, tries to stick things on, it seems to me.

Thomas: In the first place, Santa Maria in Campitelli is very solid stone, believe me. There is no stucco, no plaster on it. You have, really, a new concept of architecture, one which wishes to give the illusion—if you wish to use this work—of movement in architecture.

Hoyt: Professor MacFarlane, would you have the same criticism of the later period of Gothic?

MacFarlane: I think they ran riot in the late German Gothic cathedrals.

Heller: Perhaps you simply prefer a static quality.

MacFarlane: Yes, I think that stone is meant to give you a sense of repose.

Hoyt: What troubles me is to what degree this is a matter of personal taste and to what degree it is in the canons of art.

MacFarlane: The good art of one generation becomes the bad taste of the next.

Heller: Do you think there is any such thing as the ideal art?

Thomas: There are many ideals in art. There isn't any such thing as *the* ideal art. Obviously the classic-Renaissance style is one. As far as I am concerned, High Baroque is another idea. I don't think one style can be called intrinsically superior to the other. They happen to be enormously divergent in many ways, and are often fully contradictory.

Heller: Let me ask this. The critic presumably tries to isolate and define what our ideals are. One of the questions I have deals with this concept of ideals. Take any one of the styles that so definitely dominated—the Gothic, the Renaissance, or the Baroque. Was there a consensus in those periods of what constituted the ideal of art, a consensus that we miss today? Aren't there so many diverse architectural styles at present that it is impossible to arrive at any general consensus as to what constitutes the ideal?

Thomas: I think that is true. We are living in an incredibly sophisticated age.

Heller: That is why I am asking the question. I was trying to see why the architectural ideals that are made reflect the age.

MacFarlane: Well, they do. Frank Lloyd Wright talked about the "peacock alley" and the Gold Coast of the sophisticated East Coast of America. What he was trying to imply, I think, is that some architects feel that they must jump on the bandwagon and introduce any kind of architectural form which the wealthy donor finds pleasing. Whether it is good or not, they will do it. I think this is dishonest and that a good architect wouldn't do this. At least, Frank Lloyd Wright says he found this outrageous.

Thomas: I don't believe the really great architects can do a dishonest job.

MacFarlane: One of the most attractive things that I find in modern architecture, the best kind of modern architecture, is its honesty. It's functional; it's honest; and very often, as in the case of St. John's in Collegeville, it is also beautiful.

Heller: I suppose this is a very subjective thing. What does an expert in art, in architecture, define essentially as movement? What gives him the sense of movement? You said the Baroque had that.

Thomas: As an example, if you build a flat wall but, by means of curves and of light and shadow, create the illusion that the wall moves in and out, you have used the reactions of our optic nerves to produce in us an expectation that the wall is not necessarily a stable one. This appears consistently in the best Baroque architecture. This new attitude toward a wall is one of the ideals. The wall will appear to fluctuate, to be anti-stable, and deliberately so.

Heller: In other words, in the Renaissance structure you have a wall. There you are. However, in the Baroque structure, the wall takes on a different sense and a different feeling.

MacFarlane: I can understand the reaction against the heavy façade of the High Renaissance. Even so, I still stick to my point that the Baroque was trying to do things which you cannot really do with stone—that is, bend and curve it.

Thomas: You can do those things. The walls stand until the present day, obviously.

MacFarlane: In other words, there is some straining, some conceitedness.

Thomas: No, not necessarily. Let's look, for example, at another exterior which will make this point, the changeability, clearer. Bernini's Sant' Andrea is one of the greatest. It was a very small church, a chapel church. It belonged to the Papal palace on the Quirinal Hill. In one view, for example, the porticos stand

Sant'Andrea al Quirinale by Bernini, 1678, two views.

out sharply. One senses the flatness of this secondary area, which is the actual demarcation of the portico, and the surrounding walls, which put it in an oval, are definitely diminished. If you have another view of the chapel, it suddenly becomes considerably more solid and almost semi-Renaissance. You find yourself close to the center.

Heller: I would like to ask Leslie what it is that he dislikes about this. I happen to like this much better, by the way.

Thomas: This is one of the greatest of all Baroque structures.

Heller: Is this dishonest? Is this too pretentious?

MacFarlane: Above the center of the doorway, if I am not mistaken, there is . . .

Thomas: . . . a lovely curve.

MacFarlane: My adjective would be an "unnecessary" one.

Thomas: No, it is not at all unnecessary because it moves up and tends to lengthen the highly circular front which exists as the forward space with the rear part of the apron of the church. In other words, Bernini is an architect with a sense of spatial unity by which he has to use various curving elements, and they have to move together once more almost to a single whole. The single whole would be vastly different when you walked past it, because one of the prime characteristics that you find in fine Baroque is that it is not a stable piece of architecture but always exists in a very direct relationship with the spectator. As you move around or by it, it will change its nature.

Hoyt: I wonder if it would be too far-fetched to suggest an analogy or a parallelism with the successive changes in intellectual history. I am thinking specifically of the rationalism of the thirteenth century, followed by the movement that philosophers sometimes call "voluntarism," in the fourteenth century among nominalists. The High Renaissance in art expresses a kind of rationalism. Couldn't this Baroque style be considered as a voluntaristic reaction against intellectualism?

Thomas: Let's look at an example of a High Renaissance building. That would be the Palazzo Farnese, which is a glorious building, but perfectly stable and absolutely self-sufficient. It doesn't matter if you are there or not. There is always going to be this great rectangle, isolated, aloof, static, indifferent to us. There is no involvement whatsoever. It is marvelously proportioned. Beautiful! But it is a different architectural expression. There is rationality, stability, unchangeableness. It cannot change.

MacFarlane: You mean it is rather like Beethoven's Ninth Symphony. Once that symphonic moment was completed, later composers had to move on.

Thomas: We have to find another solution, because this is the perfect solution, almost the end solution. It can't become more perfectly rectangular, more beautifully balanced than this is.

Heller: Certainly one could say that of any good example of Renaissance architecture.

Thomas: The thing is finite.

Hoyt: Can Baroque be understood as an effort to get away from the finite and to suggest the infinite?

MacFarlane: Yes, definitely. For instance, the east window of St. Peter's gives a kind of mystical light.

Thomas: This was mostly in religious structures, naturally. There is often something comparable—not mysticism; you can call it romanticism, if you wish. The

Palazzo Farnese in Rome, c. 1530-1580. Architects: Antonio da Sangallo,
Michelangelo, and Giacomo della Porta.

opulence, the brilliance, begins to take one away from these beautiful squares
and rectangles. The form begins to merge. One thing would become something
else.

MacFarlane: Could you tell us about the interiors?

Thomas: Here is a characteristic Baroque shape, an oval, which the Baroque
loved. Unlike the geometric circle, which is a purely static shape, the oval creates
tensions. Here, for example, you have a series of interacting ovals moving one
on the other.

Heller: Hylton, has anything happened in terms of the techniques of construction
or the materials used in the construction? Could they account for the change in
shape from the Renaissance to the Baroque?

Thomas: The change is not due to technology; it's the change of temper, style,
ideal.

MacFarlane: Yet, I think you have to admit that these Baroque architects were
geniuses in the way they played with shapes.

Thomas: Definitely! After Padre Pozzo's book[1] on the mathematics of certain kinds of perspectival spatial illusions, many complex vaultings were rapidly built north of the Alps. Moreover, as you suggested, often the pictures in an illustrated book made a style expand quite rapidly. It is not a matter, necessarily, of new things; it is much the same material.

Chiesa di San Carlino alle quattro Fontane in Rome by Borromini.

---

[1] *Perspectiva Pictorum et Architectorum,* 2 volumes (Rome, 1693-1702).

Heller: In that respect, it is different from the shift from Romanesque to Gothic because the latter was entirely new in its architectural principles.

Thomas: They did endeavor to make complicated vaulting, but again, it's a matter of putting one beautiful stone on top of another. If you look into the interior of San Carlo again, you see it is not a static material there. It really does undulate backward and forward. This often permits the architect to fit secondary shapes—sacristies, little side chapels, staircases, for example—nicely into a city plan, into a restrictive plot. That is one of the reasons why the Baroque style is a splendid urban style as far as that goes—unlike the High Renaissance, which is rather demanding since all its elements have to be perfectly proportioned.

Heller: It can get into different shapes, but it demands more space.

Thomas: This is an extremely small church.

Heller: How large is this church in terms of monumentality?

Thomas: The Baroque also wants to appear large no matter how small it may be.

MacFarlane: The columns are exaggerated, the apse affected.

Thomas: It is actually very shallow, although it tends to appear very deep.

Heller: I wasn't talking about this specific example. There are very grand examples where the outside, the whole outside view of the structure, is of great spaciousness. I had the feeling in those examples that the Baroque architecture was using a lot more space than the Renaissance.

Thomas: If it can, it certainly will, but if it is restricted as here where there had to be a church, a cloister, and a conventual structure on a rather narrow plot of ground, Borromini was marvelously adept in fitting these into one another.

MacFarlane: I don't want to be too unkind, Hylton, but is this not what modern architecture calls "fussy" architecture, "busy" architecture, with things that really don't do anything?

Thomas: No, everything does something, but it is a new rhythm, a very exciting rhythm, one with a good deal of change. You move from pilaster to an engaged column; walls curve this way and then curve that way; then you reach the climax. Usually, in the great buildings a climax is somehow achieved at the altar or at the main portico on the exterior of the church or at the main portal of the palace.

Heller: I have somewhat the same reaction you have, that—if we are going to accept the term "busy,"—it is awfully hard to get a harmony, a certain unity, when there are so many diverse elements. I do speak as a layman here.

MacFarlane: It's so diverse that, in fact, it destroys the interior harmony to my mind.

Heller: Are you suggesting that harmony can only be achieved in a static situation?

MacFarlane: I think so.

Heller: I think it is a kind of dynamic harmony.

Thomas: These things are carefully calculated. These ovals are calculated on the basis of geometric inter-locking pure circles, or half geometric circles, for example. The great architects like Borromini or Bernini were deliberate and left nothing to chance.

MacFarlane: I know this and I admit—as I have said—that these men were very clever mathematicians. They knew what they were doing. Yet on top of this they destroyed it, to my mind, by contriving all kinds of dodges which they had no need to do at all.

Thomas: They wanted to make it exciting and dramatic.

MacFarlane: The staircase isn't just a straight staircase, but it tapers off, and the columns at the end—like those in the Scala Regia in the Vatican—are smaller to give the illusion of grandeur. When you walk up the Scala Regia, you find that it is only an ordinary staircase. You have been cheated.

Thomas: No. You haven't been cheated. As a matter of fact, you are making a point that I hope to deal with later, that is, the fact that the Scala Regia had to appear to be grandiose because it was the chief means of communication between the Pope and the populace, from his primary palace, the Vatican, to his primary church, St. Peter's. What Bernini had to do there was to suggest great breadth and depth in a highly constricted space, which he does gloriously well. The space becomes suitable for the greatest prelate of the West. He sweeps down the stairs into the church. There is some very practical reasoning in that, I think.

Heller: You call it trickery.

MacFarlane: I call it ostentation. It is really ingenious, but a little ostentatious, I think. Well, these things perhaps reflect one's personality.

Thomas: It is exciting as it breaks the middle; there is strong light in the foreground, another blaze of light halfway back, a great flash of light at the rear, with dark areas in between.

Heller: They are so deliberately placed.

Thomas: Obviously, their purpose is to give a systematic sequence of light, dark, light.

MacFarlane: Couldn't we move just a moment or two to sculpture, Baroque sculpture? This is another feature I find rather distressing. Nothing is left to the imagination. Take the bust of Costanza Buonarelli, done by Bernini. She is a beautiful woman. Her flesh is so soft that you can almost feel it. It's marble. It's lovely, succulent, enticing. I don't think he meant this with marble.

Thomas: He does it better than any other sculptor. I think Bernini and Michelangelo are two of the greatest sculptors of western Europe, after some of the medieval sculptors. Obviously, you are going to prefer classic sculpture. I may very well prefer just as inordinately Baroque sculpture.

Heller: I am amused that Leslie doesn't like Bernini because he does what can't be done. There is nothing wrong with that, you know.

MacFarlane: I am saying what he does. Marble is a medium which I don't think is the proper medium for a human reclining form. It's too plastic and free-flowing a form for a hard substance. This is what I would call, not dishonesty, perhaps, but . . .

Hoyt: Would you have preferred to carve it out of wood?

MacFarlane: I have another objection. An example of it is Bernini's Santa Teresa in Ecstasy. Here he has the angel with a dart poised over her heart, and she herself is swooning in ecstasy. Now this seems to me so sentimental.

Thomas: Oh, it's enormously emotional and tremendously sensuous, and is, I think, the most brilliant and fascinating expression of the mysticism of Saint Teresa herself wrote about, I think quite fascinatingly, that I know of. It's a new spiritual state of mind; it's the emotional state of mind, a religious state of mind that comes into being, and Baroque art expresses it. It is no longer the solemn, quiet, or static world of High Renaissance form.

Heller: That was rather persuasive! I agree very largely with the position you have been taking, Leslie, about the dishonesty—in the architecture, particularly, the façades which disturb me. But in the sculpture it is more interesting; one calls it sentimentalism and the other calls it emotionalism?

MacFarlane: What I think is dishonest about it is that St. Teresa was a very practical woman and she just didn't swoon in that kind of ridiculous pose.

Thomas: You must permit an artist to have artistic license. He is translating a literary statement into three-dimensional and pictorial terms and I think he does it superbly.

MacFarlane: Oh, it's a wonderful piece of work, but it is phony.

Thomas: No. Anything but phony.

Heller: It's a glorious piece of sculpture in plastic terms.

Thomas: Perhaps we should get on to some other things. One other aspect I want to bring out is the idea of fantasy that you often find in Baroque architecture, as in the cloister of San Carlo, for example. You find Borromini, in this very narrow space, pulling the corners out, denying the narrowness of the shape so that one has the feeling of space, an implication of bigness, in one of the smallest cloisters that exists in the world. If you have balusters, every second one is upside down to add a little filip, a little interest, to a rather sombre and relatively sober interior. It is true that it's fantasy. However, it is fantasy which is held in check by a real genius, a very expressive fantasy. It is not, I think, overladen and not dishonest.

MacFarlane: It's a little contrived.

Thomas: It has to be or it isn't a work of art.

MacFarlane: I am sure great art doesn't appear to be contrived.

Interior of Chiesa di San Carlo alle quattro Fontane by Borromini.

Thomas: There is one other point I want to make about San Carlo, and that is that at the same time you have also a perfect interrelationship between the arts. On this particular façade, in addition to the architectural frame itself, sculpture is lavishly used in the niches, including, of course, the statue of the major saint, St. Charles Borromeo, and there is a very nice architectural painting, a mosaic, on the upper part of the façade.

Heller: I would like to go back to the question I was raising here earlier, however, and that is this relationship between painting, sculpture, and architecture. Did it come from the Gothic or the Rennaissance?

Thomas: This is a new phase, if you want to call it that, in which architects often like to merge the three arts. This is one of the reasons that each one of these architects was in fact a sculptor or a painter or both. Borromini was a stuccatore—that is, he started as a manipulator of stucco; Bernini was a great sculptor and painter of sorts. However, this is sometimes not the case. Pietro da Cortona, for example, was a great painter but he wasn't a sculptor; nevertheless, he often used sculpture as well as painting in his churches and in his secular structures. This mixing of the arts occurs frequently enough so that it is common to the style.

MacFarlane: Hylton, could I take you up on this matter of painting? I want to continue my theme. Take the painting on the dome of Sant' Ignazio. I think it is the Apotheosis of St. Ignatius. The painter there has given the illusion of clouds and angels and of people as if the viewer were going up into heaven. What he has done, in fact, is to destroy the shape of the vault.

Thomas: That is because he wants to link heaven and earth. How else can he break away from the finite and have infinity within the solid walls of a church? You start with earth on the ground; you end with heaven where the ceiling should be, which is a splendid example of another kind of timelessness.

MacFarlane: It acts in the same way as the Gothic steeple, which tapered to the sky and led your eye up. Yes, I do see that.

Thomas: Now, perhaps, we can say something about Sant' Agnese. Here is a fine example of the unified arts of the Baroque: great sculpture, painted altars, an illusionistically painted ceiling, lavish use of bronze, gilt bronze, semi-precious materials, and yet a space which is still very big, very powerful. In three-dimensional terms, the interior is easily read as a rather complicated variation of a centralized space, so that, although the ornamentation is powerful, it is still controlled and still concentrates on the major altar.

MacFarlane: I'm sorry. It looks like a mess to me.

Heller: Isn't the use of color very important? Does the architect make this or does he have to put the sculpture in on an equal basis?

Thomas: Bernini, for example, was usually the chef. He had artists who were subordinate to him, and usually they worked very much in his style. Sometimes this was not the case.

Heller: I was trying to get at Leslie's question. He said it looks like a mess. I think it looks like a mess because of the fact that there wasn't an integration by the architect. The architect wasn't as dominant as he was in some of the earlier styles.

MacFarlane: I think it's just too powerful for words. Of course, I was exaggerating. I do know that church. The colors are very beautiful in it, but they are all too powerful; they're discordant to my mind. They fragment the mind.

Thomas: I don't think so necessarily. What the architects do is employ all possible materials, the widest possible range of color, of texture, to create a new, directly appealing church interior, a new precept of a religious structure, one that appeals to the religious spirit through the senses as much as anything.

MacFarlane: That's probably it. Could you tell us something about color?

Thomas: Well, it is used often in highly variegated and strongly colored marbles, in the lavish use of bronze, frequently gilded and sometimes of even more precious materials like lapis lazuli. The silver statues and the silver and gold altar equipment are examples of this.

Heller: The color was to serve some element of illusion?

Thomas: It does this. It is ultimately meant to suggest the infinite beauty of heaven itself, far richer, far more glorious, far wealthier, in a sense, than this poor reflection we have here on earth.

The church, Notre Dame du Haut, at Ronchamps, France, by Le Corbusier
(1887-   ).

Heller: Where do you find Baroque reflected in modern architecture? Where does the Baroque reappear? What reawakens it?

Thomas: I think, for example, you have it in what may be called free-form architecture, as in Le Corbusier's church at Ronchamps, a church with its infinitely

varied planes wandering skyline, sudden sharp movements, and strange pro-
trusions. Granted that it is not a Baroque structure, it has, I think, some of the
basic principles that you find in Baroque architecture. At the opposite end of the
pole, you have a clean, rational, functional architecture like Mies van der Rohe's
Tugendat House.

Heller: Isn't height important in our modern architecture?

Thomas: Some of the recent examples show this more and more. Some of the
things that Stone is doing, the elaborate screens for example, have certain of the
qualities of spatial illusion in which the Baroque world was interested, but this
is only one of two or three major strains that we have now. In the past, of course,

Tugendhat House at Brunn, Czechoslovakia, by German architect Mies Van
der Rohe (1886-   ).

a single style was normally the dominant strain. Most architects, greater or lesser,
practiced it to a predominant extent.

Heller: Now, Leslie, do you like the modern forms any better than the true
Baroque?

MacFarlane: No, I must confess it is still untidy and messy. I rather presume,
Hylton, with all your persuasiveness and charm, I am still not convinced that
the Baroque isn't suffering from megalomania, ostentation, vulgarity, and grandeur.

Thomas: All I can say is: Once a classicist, always a classicist.

Heller: Surely your attitude, Hylton, is in contrast to that held about 30 or 40 years ago, or even 20 years ago. Baroque today is enjoying a revival.

Thomas: As a matter of fact, it has been popular long enough so that it is really no longer truly chic among the people who are always after the last thing. It has been established for 30 years or so now as a style of real consequence.

Time, Timing, and Timeliness

Why is measurement of public opinion important?

SPEAKERS:
    ROY E. CARTER, PROFESSOR OF JOURNALISM AND SOCI-
    OLOGY, AND DIRECTOR OF THE SCHOOL OF JOURNALISM COM-
    MUNICATION RESEARCH DIVISION
    ROBERT COURSEN, EDITOR OF THE MINNEAPOLIS *Trib-*
    une's MINNESOTA POLL
    ROY G. FRANCIS, PROFESSOR OF SOCIOLOGY

COMMENTATORS: *PAUL A. GILJE*, DIRECTOR OF RESEARCH AND PUBLICATIONS
    FOR THE CITIZENS LEAGUE OF MINNEAPOLIS AND HENNEPIN
    COUNTY
    E. W. ZIEBARTH, DEAN OF THE UNIVERSITY'S COLLEGE OF
    LIBERAL ARTS

OPENING SKIT:

[A survey interviewer is at the door of a Minneapolis home.]

Knock, knock, knock.

Hello! I'm Beverly Koser, I'm a reporter from the Minnesota Poll, and I would like to ask your opinion on a few questions.

Oh, for heaven sakes! I can't hardly believe it. Won't you come in? I was just saying to Polly, my wife, the other night that we have known of hardly anyone who has been interviewed in one of these surveys, and now you come along.

This spring, Minnesota had one of its worse floods in history. Did you personally suffer any losses from the floods?

No! We were lucky in this neighborhood.

It's been proposed that the government pay off mortgages on homes that were destroyed by the floods. Do you think that that type of aid should or should not be given to flood victims?

Absolutely not!

Do you have any ideas how funds might be controlled better in the future?

Yes, I have.

What are your ideas?

Well, for one thing, I think there has been too much drainage, and for another thing . . .

DISCUSSION

Professor Hurwicz: Tonight we have with us a veritable galaxy of specialists and non-specialists on the subject of measuring public opinion. The task of distinguishing the specialists from the non-specialists, however, is more hazardous than it has ever been before. We saw a moment ago how the Minnesota Poll starts its operation when it enters a citizen's home. I have often wondered how these things work and what philosophy is behind the operation of the poll. Mr. Coursen, would you tell us about that?

Mr. Coursen: Those questions were actually part of our Minnesota survey of public opinion. One week from this coming Sunday, June 7, 1965, we will be recording how Minnesotans reacted to questions on flood control and what we might do about flood relief.

In that survey, we interviewed 600 men and women, in all walks of life. There was an interior decorator, a wife of a baker, a meat cutter, a dairy farmer—all types of people. They live in Minneapolis, St. Paul, the suburbs. Interviewers went to International Falls and Fairmont. We covered Minnesota from the Wisconsin border to the Dakota border. These 600 people comprise of what we refer to as a representative cross section of voting-age Minnesotans. That is, if we asked these questions of all men and women living in the state, the results would be essentially the same as obtained in the survey. Here are a few recent examples of published Minnesota reports on what state residents are thinking. Last Sunday when daylight time was staggered into Minnesota, we were able to report that public opinion was divided on whether our daylight-time laws should have "teeth" to threaten city officials who choose to set their own starting time for daylight time. Earlier we had the story on how Minnesotans reacted to the atom bombing of Hiroshima; 73 per cent thought that war was less likely now because our atom bomb was dropped in 1945. Still earlier, here is a report showing how Minnesotans were divided on the school bus issue. At the beginning of the year, we published results of a poll which showed that people in the state are optimistic about the present and the future in terms of national and personal finances.

The question most often asked of pollsters is: Why haven't I ever been interviewed? Why hasn't anyone I know ever been interviewed? The reaction of the gentleman in the opening skit is typical. In any given survey, we interview only a minute fraction of the population.

The next most frequently asked question goes something like this: Okay, you took a poll of the people and you know what they are thinking. So what! Most persons have no idea what power they wield as citizens and tax payers. We all know that voters have the absolute authority to say who will represent them, but I don't think we appreciate how important opinions are.

Let's look at a few examples from authorities. A chief probationary officer has said: "Without public awareness, without public concern, without public cooperation, there can be no such thing as a successful program to combat crime and delinquency."

A professor described public opinion this way: "Public opinion is outside of government; it is outside of the circle of those who make decisions; it is an opinion that moves from the outside in, from the great circle of functioning groups in society to the narrowing circle of those who finally make decisions about what government should attempt to do."

A Twin Cities chief of police pointed out: "Unless there's a general acceptance among the public, the Stop signs at railroad crossings should be obeyed, enforcement really isn't possible."

From the pen of William Shakespeare: "The body public be a horse, whereon the governor doth ride."

Sunday, January 31, 1965
MINNEAPOLIS TRIBUNE

State Optimistic Over Present and Future

Copyright 1965 Minneapolis Star and Tribune Company

"Good times are here and they are likely to get better in 1965" is the way many Minnesotans judge the financial outlook in a statewide survey by the Minneapolis Tribune's Minnesota Poll.

A representative cross-section of voting-age residents:

● Views financial conditions in the U.S. as being generally "good" in more than two out of every three interviews (68 per cent).

● Is even more inclined to expect good financial times in the 12 months ahead (76 per cent do).

Comparisons with previous Minnesota Poll surveys taken at the beginning of the year show the public's mood today to be one of the most optimistic on record.

Minnesotans' Outlook on Economy

	Good times now	Good times ahead
1963	58%	67%
1964	63	70
1965	68	76

More than six out of 10 Minnesotans (64 per cent) believe their personal finances will not change much in 1965. Adults in their 20's are an exception: 62 per cent of them expect to be better off.

The question was:

"As far as you personally are concerned, do you suppose you will be better off financially a year from now, or not so well off—or do you think there will be very little change?"

The following table does not show the responses of people who predict they will not be so well off (four per cent) and those who have no opinion or supply special answers (one per cent):

	Will be better off financially a year from now	Very little change	Total
All adults	31%	64%	95%
Men	34	60	94
Women	27	68	95
21-29 years	62	33	95
30-39 years	33	61	94
40-49 years	23	70	95
50-59 years	27	67	94
60 years and over	13	81	94
Minneapolis, St. Paul & Duluth residents	30	65	95
Smaller cities	33	60	95
Town	30	66	96
Farm	23	68	91
Adu'ts with grade school training	15	78	93
High school	32	62	94
College	46	53	99

Sunday, April 18, 1965
MINNEAPOLIS TRIBUNE

73% Say Atom Bomb on Hiroshima Makes War Less Likely Now

Copyright 1965 Minneapolis Star and Tribune Company

A majority of Minnesotans (73 per cent) think the atomic bomb attacks on the Japanese cities of Hiroshima and Nagasaki at the end of World War II have made another major war less likely to happen.

In a statewide survey of public opinion, the Minneapolis Tribune's Minnesota Poll finds 12 per cent of the people consider another world war more likely to happen because of the atom bomb.

Nine per cent can say it makes no difference and the rest (6 per cent) have no opinion.

The United States did the right thing in dropping an atomic bomb on Hiroshima in the opinion of 73 per cent of the state residents interviewed.

ANOTHER HISTORIC decision, that the United States go to the aid of the Republic of Korea after it was invaded by Communists on June 25, 1950, is termed "right" by two out of every three Minnesotans (67 per cent) and "not right" by one-fourth as many people (16 per cent).

To obtain the public's current views on two important decisions made by President Harry S. Truman did poll field reporters first asked a cross-section of voting-age men and women from all parts of Minnesota:

"Twenty years ago this summer, the first atomic bomb was dropped in warfare on the Japanese city of Hiroshima. Do you think the United States did the right thing or the wrong thing in using the atomic bomb at that time?"

The answers:

	Total	Men	Women
U.S. did right thing	73%	80%	66%
Wrong thing	15	11	18
Other answers	2	3	1
No opinion	10	6	15
	100%	100%	100%

Expressing strongest support of the Hiroshima bombing are members of the Democratic-Farmer-Labor party (81 per cent of them say "right thing"), men (80 per cent) and college-trained adults (80 per cent).

Another question was:

"Do you think the atomic bombings on

Japan made another world war more likely to happen or less likely?"

The replies:

	Total	Men	Women
More likely to have another war	12%	10%	14%
Less likely	73	77	68
"Makes no difference"	9	11	8
No opinion	6	2	10
	100%	100%	100%

Of the people who think the atom bomb attacks were wrong, more persons still believe that another major war is less likely to happen as a result (48 per cent) than consider it more likely (40 per cent).

Minnesotans also were asked:

"Do you think the United States did or did not do the right thing by entering the Korean War in 1950?"

The answers:

	Total	Men	Women
Did right thing	67%	73%	60%
Did not do right thing	16	16	16
Other answers	1	1	2
No opinion	16	10	22
	100%	100%	100%

People were more divided in their judgements on the following question:

"Do you think our country gained or lost by taking part in the Korean War?"

The responses:

	Total	Men	Women
U.S. gained by taking part	46%	48%	43%
U.S. lost	34	37	32
Other answers	6	7	5
No opinion	14	8	20
	100%	100%	100%

The feeling of gain is strongest among adults in their twenties (63 per cent) and least prevalent among people 50 and over (32 per cent).

A majority of DFLers (55 per cent) believe the U.S. gained from its efforts in Korea, while more Republicans think in terms of loss (41 per cent) than of gain (35 per cent).

"I lost a husband," a Bloomington woman said, "but as a country we didn't lose ground or gain anything except maybe prestige."

Punish DST Early Birds? State Divided

Copyright 1965 Minneapolis Star and Tribune Co.

Minnesotans are divided over how serious it is for a community to have gone on daylight saving time before today, the date prescribed by law.

"It's serious," a Fillmore county farmer told the Minneapolis Tribune's Minnesota Poll two weeks ago. "We should always abide by law and order. If we don't, how can we expect teen-agers to?" he asked.

Forty-nine per cent of a statewide sampling of adults agree that the early jump to DST by some communities is a "serious" violation of law.

Nearly as many people (47 per cent) consider it to be "not too serious." The rest of the survey respondents have no opinion or offer special views.

THE PUBLIC ALSO has a divided outlook on whether the DST law should provide for punishment of community officials who advance the starting date. Forty-three per cent are in favor of making it possible to impose fines or jail terms on violators, while 45 per cent are opposed.

This year's controversy over advanced time appears to have reduced Minnesotans' overall enthusiasm for daylight time. A representative cross-section of men and women was asked in home interviews:

"On the whole, do you like or dislike having daylight saving time during the summer months?"

The replies from two comparable surveys taken this year:

	February	May
Like daylight saving time	61%	54%
Dislike it	34	36
Other answers	—	3
No opinion	5	7
	100%	100%

In the current survey, 65 per cent of the city residents, 47 per cent of the people living in towns and 18 per cent of the farm men and women indicate they like daylight time.

The next question was:

"Duluth, Winona and other communities have started on daylight time four weeks ahead of the official date for Minnesota, contrary to state law. Do you regard that violation as serious or not too serious?"

The answers:

	All adults	I like DST	I dislike DST
Serious violation	49%	35%	67%
Not too serious	47	61	29
Other answers	2	2	2
No opinion	2	2	2
	100%	100%	100%

To a milk man who lives in Minnetonka the mixup is "just silly. It should be a national deal where the federal government sets the time," he said.

People also were asked:

"There is no punishment for city officials who violate the state law on daylight saving time. Do you think the law should or should not be changed so that officials could be fined or jailed for that violation?"

The responses:

	All adults	I like DST	I dislike DST
Should change law to allow fines or jail terms	43%	33%	61%
Should not	45	59	26
Other answers	5	5	5
No opinion	7	5	8
	100%	100%	100%

MINNESOTA POLL Release
Sunday, April 4, 1965
MINNEAPOLIS TRIBUNE

Minnesotans Divided on School Bus Issue

Copyright 1965 Minneapolis Star and Tribune Company

Minnesotans are sharply divided on the question of whether free school-bus transportation should be provided to children attending private and parochial schools.

In a statewide survey taken by the Minneapolis Tribune's Minnesota Poll, 49 per cent of the men and women interviewed are in favor of keeping school bus service just for children attending public schools.

Almost as many people (47 per cent) want free bus service provided to children going to nonpublic schools. The remaining 4 per cent either have no opinion or offer special explanations.

A Stillwater man thinks free bus service should be dispensed according to the situation within a school district. "In our area there are some buses that could carry parochial children without hardship," he said, "but in St. Paul there are so many private schools that you'd need a whole new bus system."

A housewife from Brainerd suggests taking "all students to the same 'letting-off' spot or school so that parochial school children could go on to their own school on foot."

Among Catholics interviewed, opinions divide about 8-to-1 in favor of providing

school bus transportation to all school children. Protestants favor maintaining the status quo by a 2-to-1 margin.

To learn the public's reaction on a sensitive issue before the State Legislature, the Minnesota Poll dispatched its staff of field reporters to homes in all parts of the state. People were asked:

"Which statement on this card better expresses your view about school bus transportation?"

The statements were selected in this manner:

"Free bus service should be limited to pupils attending public schools, as it is now."	49%
"Free bus service should be extended to students attending private and parochial schools."	47
Other answers	1
No opinion	3
	100%

The following table shows how different Minnesotans reacted to the question:

	Limit bus service to public schools	Extend to parochial schools	Other and no opinion
All adults	49%	47%	4%
Men	53	43	4
Women	45	50	5
Catholics	11	87	2
Protestants	63	31	6

There you have a sampling of comments that show what kind of a force public opinion is in our society today. Even in the Soviet Union, there is a public opinion. We are told that the Kremlin leaders are very much aware that there is a strong demand for consumer goods and a higher standard of living and that their foreign policies are marking time at the present moment in order to take this into account—the craving for a better life.

James Bryce summed it up very well when he said: "The obvious weakness of government by public opinion is the difficulty of ascertaining it . . ."

We know that leaders often have a very distorted view of what the public opinion is because they are exposed to a particular type of reaction. They are exposed to pressure groups. And so a public-opinion poll does a service, I believe, in setting their viewpoint into perspective. And, as citizens, we often resolve to write to our congressmen, to our legislators, to our aldermen or other representatives, but we don't get around to doing it. The public opinion poll does provide this means of letting our leaders know where we stand.

In setting up our questions we try in every way possible to be fair to all sides of the issue under scrutiny. That means impartial questions must be devised. We have an advisory board of 17 distinguished leaders who review our work and tell us where it might be improved. Dr. Carter is not a member of the Advisory Board, but he frequently gives us very helpful advice. We also try out our questions on 15 to 20 people to learn how the wording may be improved.

When we are satisfied that our questions are fair, they are asked of every man and woman in the survey in exactly the same way. That is a basic part of the discipline.

Another basic rule of the Minnesota Poll is to simply report what the public tells us. There is no editorializing or pontification. We always quote our question in our poll reports so that readers may judge how fairly they are phrased. The names of our respondents never are revealed in our poll reports. Their opinions are.

Getting back to why opinion polls are important as we proceed through time and space, I would say that never before in the history of man have the common people had as much responsibility as they do today. That is, perhaps, the most compelling reason of all for being aware of what public opinion is.

Hurwicz: I think that you have given us a very excellent idea of the philosophy behind the polling operation as it is conducted by the Minnesota Poll. Does anyone have any reaction he would like to record at this point?

Dean Ziebarth: As one of the non-specialists, whose function I assume, is to ask questions and act as a kind of gadfly, I have a comment and question. I was interested in your comment about public opinion in the Soviet Union. We so often hear relatively thoughtful and sophisticated people comment that in the Soviet Union public opinion is ignored. Not only is it *not* ignored, enormous energy and skill are poured into every kind of effort to manipulate public opinion in the Soviet Union. It is important even in authoritarian systems.

I was also intrigued by your quotation from James Bryce. It's a very interesting notion that in a democracy, to some extent, we have government by public opinion. If we took what you said literally, I suppose if we had confidence in the validity of the measuring instrument, then we would have to assume that Bryce would have us go a little bit beyond the kind of thing that is done by the

Minnesota Poll. Wouldn't it be reasonable to assume that Bryce might suggest that not only private agencies, such as your own excellent and objective Poll, should be in the business of polling, but that, in fact, this kind of work might also become an adjunct to, an arm of, possibly even a direct servant of government. This obviously has some dangers. If these questions are not appropriated at this point, Dr. Hurwicz, I would be very glad to delay. But I think these are some of the things about which I was thinking as Mr. Coursen was commenting.

Hurwicz: Perhaps, we should take you up on this. This will provide some material for us to sharpen our peers, if necessary. I think it might be a good idea at this point for us to get a clearer notion of what a poll is, not only more on the philosophy behind it, but also the mechanics, the planning, preparation and execution.

[*At this point viewers saw a series of film clips from a motion picture describing the different stages of conducting a survey. Professor Carter refers to these in the material below.*]

Professor Carter: What are the steps in conducting a survey? The first stage involves planning, library research, consulting the results of previous studies, and attempting, in short, to relate a new study to earlier studies. An important stage is the drawing of a sample. Just as one has to allow time for planning, so the timing of a drawing of a sample can be important, particularly in view of the fact that if the study is conducted shortly after the U.S. census, then we have available census materials for data that are fresh and up to date. Between censuses we have to go to the Metropolitan Planning Commission and other sources for more recent information.

In a study on the viewership of KTCA-TV, Channel 2, a telephone screening survey was used to identify regular evening viewers of Channel 2; later they were interviewed in their homes. It is important to point out that one has to take time to recruit people to do interviewing in the field. One has to take time, also, to bring them into the office to interview them and to learn something about their suitability for this kind of work.

Once the organized plan for a survey has been developed, we have to train interviewers for specific tasks. Often, of course, we do surveys that require a large number of interviewers simply because the study has to be completed in a very short period of time.

This particular study was one that could be spread over quite a few days of interviewing; thus, the number of interviewers needed was smaller than for some other surveys conducted in the School of Journalism Research Division. During the training session we distributed detailed instructions about the use of the questionnaire. We prepared them, in effect, for the task of conducting interviews. We often go into some detail with the interviewers, raising questions that have to be clarified for them. With a small number of subjects out in the community, we conducted a pre-test to make sure the questionnaire was workable and meaningful and could be understood by respondents.

The chief interviewer has the task of locating and identifying predesignated households where interviews will be conducted. One of the problems in finding the best interviewers may be in terms of the kinds of backgrounds or perhaps even the personality characteristics which are necessary for effective interviewing and gaining access to the respondent. Very often the acquiescence to the request

An interviewer training session: Professor Carter, standing, is giving instructions.

to participate isn't rapid. After being invited in, the interviewer tries to seat herself in such a way that the respondent cannot look over her shoulder at the questionnaire—something that might interfere with the procedure of the interview. She wants to interview the respondent alone. We work very hard to do this because we don't want the husband, for example, to influence his wife's responses in the survey, or vice versa.

The interviewer may seek clarification of an answer through what we call probe questions. These are designed to elaborate upon what the respondent had said in her own words and, perhaps, in a way that was not entirely clear to the person doing the interview. Incidentally, one of the additional problems is getting out of the household smoothly and quickly.

The work on analysis begins, of course, when the interviewer returns the completed questionnaires to the survey central office. In most studies, we have people who check in the questionnaires and make sure the interviewer has completed the assignments. Also, at this stage, there is the work of verifying interviews—making sure that they were conducted. We trust our interviewers, but we also make telephone checks on what was done in a sample of interview households.

We also convert people's answers into codes, into numerical names for the answers, and these numerical names later get translated into holes in IBM punchcards. It may be a young woman in a Numerical Analysis Center of the University of Minnesota who punches into IBM cards the answers given by respondents. A great deal of speed can be acquired by these girls.

Later on the cards are checked or verified, and eventually, of course, the cards turn up in the hands of someone who uses either the countersorter, some other statistical equipment, or one of the electronic computers to tabulate and analyze the answers.

Hurwicz: This is certainly helpful information for giving us a complete idea of how surveys are planned and executed.

Mr. Gilje: Though I am not an expert in this area, Dr. Carter, your explanation is quite interesting to me and completely impressive. But how do we know that a poll or survey is accurate? I can imagine that there are probably some pretty well-informed critics of some public-opinion polling who might just go off and find some good many loopholes in this procedure.

Carter: Indeed, we have critics, and they have some major criticisms. I can say, however, with some sense of self-assurance, that criticisms are fewer and less serious than they used to be. Certainly, they are not of the magnitude and seriousness of criticisms that were raised after public opinion polls in this country predicted the election of Thomas Dewey in 1948.

Hurwicz: This brings us to the point where we might try to focus on the chief objective of this series which deals with the time aspect of various social phenomena. We will hear a little bit about the time aspect of the public opinion surveys. With regard to Mr. Gilje's comment and query, the explanation is often a matter of timing of a very rapid trend just before the election. An example is the California primary when Senator Goldwater's victory was not completely predicted. This brings us the question of the time pattern of public opinion. Mr. Carter, could you tell us about this?

Carter: Certainly. Although our concern here today is largely with time and timing in relation to the *surveys* designed to measure public opinion, there are other "time" factors in this field, too. For example, a good many political analysts have been interested in—and at the same time puzzled by—the *stability* of public opinion on many issues and also the ways in which patterns of opinion change develop through time. The chart on Labor and Democratic Party vote shows some consistencies and some possible trends in public opinion in Norway and England as revealed, not by public opinion polls, but by actual voting results in elections. As can be seen from the two lines in the graph, there has been an over-all upward trend in voting strength of the labor parties in the two countries. What is more interesting, however, is the fact that the gains and losses from election year to election year were in general modest. All of this had led to some interesting efforts by a Swedish sociologist, Gosta Carlsson, to develop some mathematical models capable of describing the ways in which changes of this kind occur. Carlsson proposes a "response" model to deal with the "diffusion" and "equilibrium" phases of a political or social movement, and uses it to show why departures from an even split of opinion are small even when momentary forces work strongly in favor of one party.

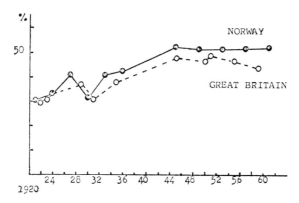

Labor and Democratic Party vote, Norway and Great Britain,
1920-1962.

Incidentally, Professor Carlsson's article[1] appears in a recent issue of the magazine *Public Opinion Quarterly*, along with another article by a history professor at the University of California who is trying to explain the patterns of stability and change in North American voting behavior from the early days of our republic down to the present time.[2]

In the same magazine—a section devoted to the actual findings of studies in the field of public opinion—a series of statistics from a variety of national polls shows a remarkable consistency through recent years in the extent to which the people of our country indicate such religious beliefs as a faith in the existence of God and a conviction that there is a life after death. Questions of this kind exhibited far more differences *across countries*—that is, comparing one people's opinions with those of another—than down through time in our own United States. The chart you see here shows the stability in answers Americans gave to these questions in national surveys rather widely separated from one another in time.

A discussion of *time* in relation to public opinion polls would not be complete if we failed to mention the fact that in a good many fields, particularly the arena of political opinions, in recent years definite changes have occurred in the purposes for which many surveys are conducted and the auspices under which they are carried out. Specifically, I am referring to the fact that in the periods prior to elections in this country an increasingly large proportion of the public opinion research is being done by and for interested parties—that is, political parties, candidates, and organized groups supporting various candidates—and proportionately less of the research is being carried out under academic auspices

[1] Gosta Carlsson, "Time and Continuity in Mass Attitude Change: The Case of Voting," *Public Opinion Quarterly*, 29:1, Spring, 1965, pp. 1-15.

[2] Charles Sellers, "The Equilibrium Cycle in Two-Party Politics," *Public Opinion Quarterly*, 29:1, Spring, 1965, pp. 16-38.

PERCENTAGE OF INTERVIEWED PERSONS EXPRESSING SELECTED
RELIGIOUS BELIEFS IN U.S. PUBLIC OPINION POLLS
IN DIFFERENT YEARS*:

Belief in a Supreme Being	1944	96%
	1948	96%
	1954	96%
Belief in life after death	1936	64%
	1944	76%
	1948	68%
	1957	74%
	1960	74%

* From Hazel Gaudet Erskine, "The Polls: Personal Religion,"
data summarized in *Public Opinion Quarterly*, 29:1, Spring, 1965,
pp. 145-49.

or as part of ongoing public opinion polls like the Minnesota Poll or the published polls of the Gallup organization.

In 1959, Louis Harris, one of the principal doers of private polls in the field of politics, had a good deal to say about how the "old survey order was changing."[3] He noted, for example, that in the 1956 and 1958 pre-election polls in this country, about $300,000 was spent on newspaper-type polls, $600,000 for studies conducted through universities, and about $1,000,000 on private surveys for candidates and parties. The swing toward heavy political expenditures for polls had only begun back in those years, of course, and by 1964 it had reached a magnitude far beyond what Harris was talking about.

Another trend has been the steady and longterm growth of market research and research on advertising. In fact, market and consumer studies account for an increasingly large share of the total time spent in the field by survey research interviewers. Most market research is conducted in respectable ways by competent people, usually through interviews in people's homes but sometimes on the telephone as well. Unfortunately, we have had trouble in recent years with salesmen who employ the ruse or pretense of a survey in order to make some kind of sales pitch on the phone. This practice was so extensive in the Twin Cities a few years ago that when we conducted a telephone survey about the viewing of programs on KTCA-TV we had to *eliminate* an opening question that asked whether the person we were talking to had a television set in his home.

Remember, this difficulty arose even though we explained the survey was being done under auspices of the University of Minnesota. Despite this, many people chose to hang up the telephone after telling us that they did not want to buy a TV set. The misuse of the term "survey" in sales campaigns has become

---

[3] Louis Harris, "Is the Old Survey Order Passing?", *Political Research: Organization and Design*, 2:4, March, 1959, pp. 8-10.

serious enough to prompt a distinguished sociologist at the University of Washington, Stuart Dodd, to suggest that the telephone company work out a plan whereby people could have stars printed opposite their names in the telephone book to indicate that they do not want to be solicited by telephone salesmen. Subscribers who did not want to take part in any kind of survey could have their names *double* starred. As a researcher, I do not think I would want to give people that second option, for it might eliminate the possibility of drawing representative samples for telephone surveys. Face-to-face interviews are generally preferable to phone studies, but the latter *can* be useful, too.

My mention of market surveys and advertising research leads me to point out two things: first, the need for information about the audiences of the mass media of communication was one of the main factors leading to large-scale development of survey research here in the United States. Second, the fact that audience studies—studies that deal with who watches what on television or who reads what in the newspaper—are types of research that involve especially difficult problems in connection with survey *timing*.

It is well-known that studies of the audiences of the mass media in this country had most of their origins in the development of radio. When that new medium of communication appeared on the scene in the early 1920's, some manufacturers of radio sets believed that the business could be supported by the *sale* of radios. That is one reason why it was a company like Westinghouse that first went on the air with commercial broadcasting. It soon became apparent, however, that the industry was to depend on advertising as its principal source of revenue. Also, radio just did not have the circulation data that newspapers and magazines had. People who advertised or bought time on radio in the early days were purchasing what my Southern friends call a "pig in a poke"—something the nature of which is completely unknown.

There was a real need for the development of survey methods which could produce reasonably reliable data about the size and composition of the listening audiences for different stations and different programs. In other words, data on the sale of radio sets or on the power of the signals of the radio stations were not sufficient to give the prospective radio advertiser the kind of information needed. Survey procedures to measure radio listening were developed at a fairly rapid pace. Soon they provided the radio industry with more detailed information about its audiences than newspapers and magazines had about theirs. The data collected contained information about the age, sex, educational background, occupation, and buying power of listeners.

As a result, newspapers and magazines began to study their audiences with some intensity, using survey procedures. Audience research for one mass medium has led to audience research for other media. Some research clients, research specialists in government and on university staffs, and some of the philanthropic foundations have also become concerned with basic research on mass communication, especially in recent years. At the University of Minnesota, some basic research has been sponsored by the Minneapolis newspapers.

Those who read the so-called Madow report a few years ago realize that the procedures used in measuring radio and TV audiences have their weaknesses, some of which were clarified or even magnified in hearings before a committee of the U.S. Congress. I tend to agree with those critics of radio and television who feel that the sameness and the low quality of much program content must be blamed on the people who use and misuse the so-called rating services. A "rating," of course, is simply an estimate of the size of the audience for a particular program.

The way timing becomes important in conducting research about mass media audiences is fairly easy to see. If we over-stimulate the respondent, if we provide him with too many reminders of programs he could have watched or of the things he might have read, there is some risk that we are going to lead him to make false claims about his reading or listening behavior. This was illustrated a few years ago in a Southwestern state when a substantial proportion of the people interviewed in a survey looked at a list of programs allegedly on TV several nights before and claimed that they had listened to and watched a speech by President Eisenhower, even though the President had not made a talk on that occasion.

We can never learn what people have read, or listened to, or watched if we wait so long after the event itself as to make it likely that the thing we are questioning them about will be confused with programs or printed material encountered in the intervening time. Our principal way of dealing with this problem is to get the study to the field as soon as possible and complete it right away. We try to interview people about their TV viewing or their newspaper reading on the day following the actual exposure to such content. This maximizes the likelihood of accurate recall of what the person actually did and minimizes the chances that the individual will confuse today's headline with yesterday's, or last week's TV show with the one that was on last night.

The kind of survey in which the field work has to be completed in a short period of time has obvious implications for the recruitment and training of interviewers. Having reached a decision on the number of respondents we want in our sample, we have to contract and prepare interviewers for the study and get them in the field in sufficient number so as to make it possible to complete the work in the time allotted. Our newspaper readership surveys usually involve attention to every page of the previous day's newspaper and to an accompanying public opinion questionnaire that may require 15 to 20 minutes additional time from the person who is interviewed. In that kind of study, where our sample size is typically between 200 and 300, we find that the average interviewer is able to do a maximum of 10 interviews in a single 24-hour period. This means that we must use up to 30 interviewers in the project.

Another way in which surveys relate to time is the fact that survey research findings in general lack what has been called "time's arrow." That is, surveys simply will not enable us to prove that anything that was published or broadcast actually caused changes in people's behavior unless we are in a position to make "before" and "after" measurements—that is, question people before the material goes out and then afterward. Ideally, of course, we also need to study a control group—that is, a group not exposed to the material at all. Sometimes we are able to do this by means of what we call a field experiment.

A recent Minnesota example of field experimentation was a study in which the researcher attempted to influence the watching of evening broadcasts on KTCA-TV by an experiment which required the cooperation of public school people. The experimental conditions essentially were ones in which high school students either did or did not receive encouragement from their teachers to watch certain public affairs programs on Channel 2. Where such encouragement was given, the teacher endeavored to make viewing a socially rewarding experience by providing follow-up discussion opportunities with teaching aids that our staff had prepared. Before and after the weeks of these TV programs, more or less conventional survey techniques were used to study the opinions and viewing behavior of children and their parents—those who had been exposed to the stimulus and those who had not. Since the researcher had manipulated factors which might influence what these people watched and how they responded to the content, he was able to trace the effects of his efforts on viewing behavior. The effects might be summarized in this fashion: We affected viewing behavior as we intended, but not on a long-term basis. Below, the experimental design in somewhat simplified form is shown:

	Experimental Group	Control Group
VIEWING HABITS BEFORE EXPERIMENT	Measured	Measured
	"Stimulation period"	
VIEWING HABITS SOON AFTER EXPERIMENT	Measured	Measured
VIEWING HABITS MONTHS LATER	Measured	Measured

Another frequently used field experiment in communication research is one involving the so-called "split run" in which half the copies of a publication contain an advertisement or other content in one form, and the other half carries a different version. Ordinary field interviewing procedures are then used to determine which version was read most, believed most, or acted upon most.

These are some of the ways in which time and timing can strengthen or undo survey research efforts.

Ziebarth: You were talking about training the interviewers for maximal validity in response. This is just a possibility of the variety of sources which might be described as false responses. But isn't it necessary that you yourselves in the construction of the materials with which the interviewers deal must have equal care?

I remember, for example, when the old Psychological Corporation was still operating that at the time of the publication of *Gone With the Wind*,[4] there was a fantastic question involved which was in effect: Have you read *Gone With the Wind?* Something like 98.1 per cent of the respondents said yes which everyone knew was nonsense. That question was changed in the next sample to read: Do you intend to read *Gone With the Wind?* They had, approximately, the same response.

---

[4] Margaret Mitchell (New York: Macmillan and Co., 1939).

I remember that you mentioned the introduction of measurement of this kind as an outcome of the development of radio and that we needed to determine aspects of the audience. In some surveys, programs which were never produced, but about which questions were asked, had enormously high ratings, particularly if they had pretentious titles. I remember, for example, one called "Education for You in the Modern World," or something of that kind which was just a figment of the imagination of one of the consultants to a group of that kind. The fictitious program had a rating which would be respectable by any commercial standards. I wonder whether you don't find it necessary to guard against this sort of sample?

Carter: Those are real problems. An example of the kind of difficulty which was illustrated by the study of the *Gone With the Wind* question is the asking of questions relating to viewing or reading the media. We discovered a long time ago that if we ask the respondent whether he *usually* does something, and then ask him—let's say—whether he did it *yesterday,* we have much more chance of getting a valid response to the *yesterday* question. The reason is that if the question deals with something he feels he ought to do, he can give vent to the impulse to get that idea across in answering the first question. Error, of course, creeps in the survey in many ways. The whole survey operation is a communication process, and in any communication venture there are many, many places in which error or misunderstanding can occur. It's not just what the interviewer does. The person designing the questionnaire may be responsible, and error also arises from sampling. One of the misconceptions, however, is that sampling is the main source of survey errors. A distinguished sociologist once said that the use of modern sampling procedures in some kinds of contemporary surveys is analogous to the use of a scalpel in a butcher shop. In other words, other tools aren't sharp enough in comparison with the sampling techniques, though some progress is being made along these lines.

Hurwicz: Before we get too involved in this, perhaps we should consider another point which follows logically from the kind of examples we were given earlier. We occasionally see a series of survey responses such as those indicating the percentage of persons holding a belief in deity, in which year and year, they turn out exactly the same per cent. Laymen might be forgiven for being just a trifle skeptical as to whether this phenomenon is quite so constant.

There is a counterpart to this doubt in situations where the percentage of people, for example, who favor a certain politician or law, varies tremendously from one month to the next, at least according to the polls. We may ask ourselves is this actual fact or just an illusion created by the process of polling. Professor Francis, would you comment on this problem?

Professor Francis: I will begin by recalling what Roy Carter said about sampling error. We know that from one poll to the next—if the poll is done properly and the sample drawn according to the theory of randomness—there will be a variation on just that account. In almost every aspect of life we get used to variation. If the baseball player, Harmon Killebrew, went through a game without striking out, no one would ever say there is a probability that he will never do it again. We expect that there is going to be variation from one performance to the next. The same thing is true of any poll.

There is also a possibility of a variation from one poll to the next by design. If, for example, one area in the population we are studying is known to have a different kind of response from other areas, we can change the proportion of people that we draw from the one or the other.

Hurwicz: Do you mean geographical areas?

Francis: Yes. This will affect the outcome and give the illusion of change when change hasn't really occurred.

Sometimes, as Roy Carter has suggested, the very words we use affect the outcome. One famous incident involved Franklin Roosevelt's first change in the date of Thanksgiving. In one poll the people were asked: "What do you think of having the date of Thanksgiving moved?" There was a tendency toward a favorable response. When the question was phrased: "What do you think of President Roosevelt's changing the date of Thanksgiving," the response was almost completely dictated by the political party preference of the respondents.

The words themselves can change meaning over time. Operationally, we have a peculiar difficulty with words. If we have one population, it is necessary that we use exactly the same words to each segment of the population when you are conducting a survey or risk arousing different kinds of sentiment.

Sometimes, by fault of methodology, there is indication that change has occurred when the people to whom we are talking are simply not in a position to be able to indicate that there was a change. Many adults, for example, are concerned about the "fact" that the present generation is going to the dogs. This is something that each generation is convinced of and our proof generally goes back to what we thought of when we were growing up. There have been surveys essentially of this kind. The people have been asked: "Do you notice any kind of a change?" Obviously, the kids are dancing differently than before. I suspect that the frug is really an Indian Rain Dance, and this would account for the mysterious weather we've been having.

Ziebarth: With all the rain we've had, in effect it has been.

Francis: Quite often people are tempted to compare their own childhood with the present, forgetting that they have moved in the social scheme. Ours is a success-oriented culture. We all want to move up the ladder. We may reflect on our own childhood—if we can recall accurately at all—and be talking on one kind of background. Then, having success, we observe our children in a different socio-economic class. We may not be talking about change from a period of time to the next, but simply we are referring to our own success pattern. If we aren't on guard about these problems when questions are phrased, surveys may come to the conclusion that social changes are taking place when it is an illusion.

I think we are getting sophisticated enough now that the general public will not fall into these obvious errors.

Hurwicz: You mentioned earlier the possibility that impression of change might be created simply by the vagaries of sampling. Some surveys use the panel technique of going back to the same person a bit later and asking: "Do you still think that Mr. Jones is a great major or president?" Does the Minnesota Poll use these techniques? Have they been considered?

Coursen: No, we don't. We interview fresh samples of people each time. The panel method is an effective device, but there is always a question of whether or not you have contaminated the people, in a sense, by interviewing them and exposing them to the questions. Their behavior may then be different than it would have been.

Francis: Another problem with the panel technique is that our society is mobile. If an interval between samples is any appreciable length of time, there may be a significant movement—people moving, leaving, or dying—so that you have the awkwardness of trying either to replace the sample or account for a shrinking body to work with.

Carter: You do have to worry about the effect on the people being studied. Some of the earliest studies in industrial sociology, for example, were of people working in a manufacturing plant. The researchers experimented with illumination and fussed around with other things that might make for more comfortable working conditions. Finally, the investigators discovered that the reason the people were happier was that they were getting so much attention.

Ziebarth: I can give you an illustration of that in terms of the devastating nature of immediacy of response. I happened at one time to be in a CBS studio in New York when the instantaneous audience measurement devices—which operated literally instantaneously—were being experimented with. The experimenters made the almost incredible mistake of having the reactions calibrated in such a way that the dial was moving in the studio in which the performance was being given. As this dial dropped, the performance dropped along with it until almost at the end sagged to a point of total disaster. It had a tremendous and traumatic influence.

Hurwicz: A case of a self-fulfilling prophecy?

Ziebarth: I suspected it might be, in a sense.

Francis: It is like your earlier question about the effect of a poll in a real-life situation. What is the consequence? In the Soviet Union, for example, we should distinguish between the efforts to get at the total public opinion, and the efforts to get private opinion. There is a significant difference. It's one thing to get public opinion and quite a different thing to set a strategy to find out people are really thinking about.

Hurwicz: There is a story which takes place in a totalitarian country where a citizen was asked: "What is your opinion?" He said: "Well, my opinion, with which, incidentally, I do not agree. . . ."

Carter: In market research some problems have been solved by trying to bring the question close to the deed, that is: "What brand of coffee did you buy yesterday, if you bought any yesterday?" By getting closer to the behavior or by looking at the pantry, results are more accurate. There have been actual research studies where the check was not made in the pantry but in the garbage cans for the current type under study. Different kinds of crews of couples have to be hired for that kind of study.

One thing we haven't done enough with is direct observation of human behavior. Often in the so-called behavioral sciences, we've behaved as though we thought—and we know better—that the marks made on a questionnaire by the interviewer in the field, or by an individual filling out the questionnaire himself, were actually behavior.

During World War II in Great Britain there was an organization called Mass Observation. It did fascinating research which involved direct observation. Sometimes this direct observation worked remarkably well, particularly in areas where you wouldn't be able to trace changes in response to difficult questions. For instance, they asked people if they hated Hitler. Yes, they all hated Hitler. But it was quite another matter to check up and see the variations in how many people defaced and spat upon pictures of Hitler in public places.

Hurwicz: Did they provide pictures for this purpose?

Carter: These were anti-Nazi pro-morale propaganda posters. The researchers thought, of course, that they were able to detect fluctuations in the will to fight and the anger of Britons by this kind of research.

Ziebarth: To what extent may a poll or some variant of it actually measure public opinion and to what extent it may be used to influence public opinion. A poll taken just before an election may not only measure, but also reflect opinion, that is, a poll may actually influence opinion. Can the poll be a dangerous and doubtful device in that sense? Do any of these suggestions have some validity?

Francis: It would be extremely difficult to set up a research to find out precisely to what extent this is true. I don't know of anyone who has seriously attempted to set up a definitive study of this kind. There are scads of anecdotical material that hint that this is quite likely. One case occurred in Oregon where newspapers were very faithfully giving the public opinion and the public opinion was going against its editorial policy. It became a source of chagrin. They were able to get a congressman who felt the way they did and had him call a press conference in which he made a pronouncement saying what the public wanted was just not possible. Soon after the polls changed.

Hurwicz: This was not a case of illusion then?

Francis: This was a case of self-fulfilled prophecy.

Gilje: What value does a poll have other than satisfying curiosity in an election?

Coursen: The Minnesota Poll objective is to report the best we can where the election stands and let the chips fall where they may. This in itself is a public service because there are other reports which are done for the candidates which may be leaked in somewhat unethical way to further the cause of their candidates. But our goal is to be as accurate as we possibly can.

There is far more than the horse-race aspect in an election. We try to discover what people are thinking about the issues and how different items in the campaign have affected their thinking. Any person with real conviction hardly will be swayed by whether the polls are showing their particular candidate ahead or behind.

Francis: The greater danger is what can happen to the political attitude of those who are seeking political office. They may use the public-opinion poll as a device in which they can get on the right side of the public, rather than using the political campaign as a means of education, of discourse, and for exchange.

Hurwicz: You don't imply that without polls these people wouldn't try to do it? They just would not be in as good a position to be sure that they are right—which side will draw the most votes.

Francis: They try to find out which is a safe course of events. They may follow them to the extent to which they are convinced that the polls are really tapping what people believe. It is much easier to surrender to the poll rather than for the office seeker to say his responsibility is to try to change opinion.

Carter: I don't believe that public opinion polls are in themselves affecting the course of public opinion. Political attitudes tend to be very stable. We know from studies of the whole socialization process that often these are acquired while people are very young. As a matter of fact, the best single question for predicting a man's vote is how his father voted. Still, I think there is a great need for research on the possibility of these kinds of effects, difficult as that research may be.

In talking with students about this, I often present evidence to suggest that polls don't have harmful effects. Still, I get the feeling always that I am basing my case too much upon what might have been historical accidents. The fact that neither the *Literary Digest* poll nor the nation's editorial writers elected Landon in 1936, and the fact that the polls did not elect Dewey in 1948. The point is that we don't have much to go on except the many instances of apparent discrepancy between how people behave in national voting, what the polls said, and what the newspapers said.

Francis: Imagine the difficulty of trying to assess this in any survey type of study by going to a politician with a questionnaire asking how often do you go with public opinion.

Ziebarth: I want to get back to a simple question. We talked about the validity, the assumptions of validity in relation to the polls. What influence could we have if we assume that the validity was very high? What do you find with the Minnesota Poll? You were talking, Dr. Carter, about the study which you and your colleagues conducted relevant to the viewing habits of people who do view this particular channel. What kind of validity assumptions would you like us to make about what you are doing?

Carter: In the case of that particular study, we tried to deal with the problem of validity by doing a number of things. We decided, for example, that one of the problems in connection with the studies of educational television viewers in this country was that they were largely studies of *non-viewers*, that is, the regular viewers did not turn up in very large numbers in general population samples. So what we did was set a recall criterion. We wouldn't let a person classify himself as a regular viewer of Channel 2—unless he could tell us something about the programs he had seen recently. Now, in most surveys, we work on problems of this kind. Certainly, when you are asking questions about opinion, you work very hard to find out whether people are informed about the issue before you press them for an expression of opinion.

Hurwicz: I have a question about validity. Mr. Coursen, earlier you explained the rationale of the sampling process. Roughly speaking, if you get 73 per cent holding a certain belief from a small sample, presumably, had you interrogated much larger faction of the population of this state, the percentage you would get would be quite close. To what extent have you been able to check up on this? Have you sometimes taken, for example, larger samples in the habitual size to see how much variance there is?

Coursen: The most acid test that pollsters can be put to, I think, is an election. How do you intend to vote? We found, sometimes, an accurate indication of the final answer way off in the distance. A few years ago the public's reaction to the Taconite Amendment started at a certain level of approval and stayed there right up to election day. It carried very easily. This is one demonstration.

Hurwicz: Do you correct that with the probability of voting?

Coursen: Whether the person is going to vote is taken into account in the survey. I would like to add one other point which is very important. It is what Roy Francis mentioned about the sophistication of the people. We should not underestimate the intelligence of the public. There is a wisdom in the general public we should take pride in and, generally, into which we can put confidence. They are not to have the "wool pulled over their eyes" very often.

Carter: So said George Gallup in a couple of books in which the central theme has been that the people were ahead of their government on many issues through the years.

Francis: Shakespeare was quoted as having said that public opinion can be likened to a body of a horse on which the government rides. Then the question is: What part of the anatomy . . .

Hurwicz: Several points have been raised with regard to the broad spectrum of public opinion of a random sample of the great mass and the question of leadership, whether by politicians and others. Mr. Gilje, when you are associating with a group such as The Citizens' League which cautiously takes the task of leadership, does this issue of general opinion versus opinion of a group of this kind have a place?

Gilje: We certainly hope that the leadership we take has an effect of leading the public. In developing a consensus as we try to do on issues, we try to reach a point where the opinion of our people turns out to be their leadership. I think it does turn out to be leadership.

Continuing on the point of validity, Mr. Coursen, I am quite interested in knowing whether we can expect another debacle like the 1948 election when Dewey was predicted to win? Is this possible?

Coursen: It is possible for an individual poll to be on the wrong side in any given election. As a pollster, you always hope it's not going to be the one coming up, but one way in the future. We certainly wouldn't expect a mass departure again as we had experienced in 1948.

Hurwicz: Do you feel there has been an improvement in the techniques that would account for this optimism?

Coursen: We have much more sophisticated measures now than we did previously.

Critical Times and Behavior Change

Did I make the right decision?

SPEAKERS: MRS. ELAINE C. WALSTER, ASSOCIATE PROFESSOR OF
PSYCHOLOGY IN THE OFFICE OF THE DEAN OF STUDENTS
JOHN C. WRIGHT, ASSOCIATE PROFESSOR IN THE INSTI-
TUTE OF CHILD DEVELOPMENT

COMMENTATORS: MRS. DOROTHY LEWIS, ST. PAUL *Dispatch* REPORTER
HOMER E. MASON, ASSOCIATE PROFESSOR OF PHILOSOPHY

OPENING: A SKIT

[A young couple are gazing into each other's eyes].

He: You know how I feel about you. Will you marry me?

She: Yes, yes (enthusiastically) !

[The couple embrace. Each turns aside].

She: No. Maybe I shouldn't have!

He: What am I saying?

[They turn back toward each other after a moment and embrace each other
again].

DISCUSSION

Professor Hoyt: If discussion about behavior is to be informative and purposeful,
it will necessarily include decision-making. Two psychologists will tell us about
the process of decision-making, particularly how time influences that process.

Professor Walster, would you start off by telling us how one makes up one's
mind?

Professor Walster: I will start with the effect time has on the decisions and the
choices we make. Take for example, a decision most of us have to make every time
we move—whether we want to buy a house or to rent an apartment. Usually
before we make an important decision like that, we find out all about the alternatives. We end up with a great deal of new information. Usually by the time a
decision must be made, this new information has altered our previous opinions
and predispositions.

Because of this extensive consideration of the alternatives that goes on pre-
decisionally, most people would probably think that by the time we make our
decisions, our feelings have a pretty firm basis, and that new experiences and
second-thoughts are unlikely to change our feelings radically.

Some of the research and ideas that we would like to talk about tonight will
indicate that the very act of making a decision does have a strong impact on

our attitudes. Systematic and important changes do occur in our opinions and attitudes after a decision is made.

I will tell about one of the studies that we have done. This study[1] interviewed people after they had made a decision. It was found that immediately after a person has made an important decision, he is upset and distressed and very concerned about whether or not he had made the right choice. Then after some time has passed, he loses this distress. He becomes more sure of the rightness of his choice; he is more convinced that he had made the right decision. In fact, he often ends up thinking not only that the decision was as good as he had thought at the time he made it, but that his decision was practically the only sensible one that could have been made.

Now if John Wright will help me, I'll tell you in more detail about the results of the study I just described. The people we interviewed were army recruits.

Professor Wright: I'm supposed to be an army recruit?

Walster: That's right. We interviewed men their second day in the army. They got their hair cut, they picked up some army clothes, then they came to see us. We were there as job processors. Now John, you first come to me to be assigned a job. I tell you a little bit about ten jobs I have to offer. Each one of the jobs has some glorious feature and some terrible feature. Here's our selection: One thing we might offer you, today, would be a job as a tank crewman. You have to work in very tight spaces, but you will probably get to go to Europe. Another job I could offer you is a job as a sewer maintenance man. If you choose this job, there are the obvious occupational disadvantages, but there are some advantages too: there is little work to do, you work only when there is an emergency. The last of our jobs is a job detecting and removing mines. This would be a high-paying job but it too has some obvious disadvantages.

After describing the jobs, we asked men to evaluate the desirability of the job. You should rate a job "1" if it is one of the nicest jobs you've ever heard about.

Wright: I don't think sewer maintenance man is one of them.

Walster: Then you'd rate it a little lower. If you really dislike a job, you'd rate it 30; a job that's about average should be rated 15. I'd like to add that I'm not sure I will be able to offer you all these jobs. You have to take some tests first to see if you're qualified. But for now, give me a rating of all the jobs.

Wright: I'd say that, maybe, I would like most to be a tank crewman, so I'll rate that 5. Then, maybe—it doesn't leave much choice. I'll rate sewer maintenance 10 and mine detector the lowest, a 13. It's even worse.

Walster: After rating all jobs, the soldiers then left and began taking tests. Their absence gave us a chance to pick out two jobs that had been rated fairly close together in desirability. In your case, John, I would have chosen sewer maintenance man which you rated 10 and mine detector which you rated 13. Then,

---

[1] Elaine Walster, "The Temporal Sequence of Post-Decision Processes" in Leon Festinger's *Conflict, Decision and Dissonance* (Stanford University Press, 1964).

I'd tell you that your tests had shown that these are the two jobs for which you are best qualified. Finally, I'd ask you to choose the one you wanted.

Wright: I'll choose sewer maintenance man, with some reluctance.

Walster: At this point, I write your job choice down on some very official looking forms. I send the forms out with the clerk and explain to you that your job assignment is complete and that you won't be allowed to change your mind.

Then I tell you about a little research project that we are conducting in hopes of improving our job placement program. I ask if you would be willing to help with it, and of course you are. Then I ask you to think about the job you chose for a minute more and then come back to see me and tell me a little more about your reactions to the jobs. Some soldiers were asked to come back one minute after they made their decision, others after four minutes, some after 15 minutes, and still others 90 minutes after their choice. That way we could see how their attitudes toward the job they had chosen and the job they had rejected changed over time.

Well, as I told you earlier, the passage of time allows people to change their mind in some very consistent ways. Immediately after one has made his choice, he rates the jobs very much as he did in the initial rating (when he rated all 10 jobs and before he was asked to make a choice). Not much change in a person's opinions, then, seems to occur from the initial ratings to the time when the decision is made.

Four minutes later, things are quite different. Men, subjectively, will express the feeling that they are not quite sure that they were really cut out to be a maintenance man after all. When you ask them to rate the job they chose and the job they rejected, the chosen job has gotten to be *less* desirable than it was pre-decisionally, and the rejected job has gained a little in desirability. Obviously, the men seem to regret their decision after about four minutes.

However, the feeling that they are not sure how good a decision they made doesn't last long. When you interview them 15 minutes after their decision, you find that the chosen job has gone way up in attractiveness. The rejected job is rated even lower in attractiveness than it was before the decision was made. Sometimes after 15 minutes, the soldiers have forgotten many of the good things about the job they rejected, and some of the bad things about the job they chose. By 15 minutes after a decision then, soldiers are very sure they've made a good choice.

Mrs. Lewis: This is like rationalization.

Walster: I think you can call it that if you want to. After 15 minutes, the soldiers are spreading the alternatives apart in desirability, convincing themselves that the choice they made was a very good one. We can't call what they are doing four minutes after the decision rationalization though. At that time, they are feeling they made the *wrong* choice.

Wright: It is sort of like that newly engaged couple in the opening. Their first reaction was "what have I done?" They were really worried that they had made a terrible mistake. But, the longer they thought about it, the better the idea seemed to be.

Walster: There are reasons why we usually ended up thinking we have made a splendid choice. Making a good decision is important to us for two reasons. First, we want to possess the best things we can. A good decision means we possess better things. Secondly, we probably feel that it is important to make a good decision in and of itself. Thus, we worry about how good a choice we made, even if it's too late to change our minds. We think, "Was I justified in making the choice that I did?" If it is clear the decision was right, we can quit worrying about it. But when there's not much justification, that's when it's especially important to convince ourselves that we did the right thing.

Hoyt: Is there any correlation between these changes that you indicated take place after the elapse of different amounts of time and the soldier's ATC scores and other measurements of I.Q.?

Walster: We received information about the intellectual ability of soldiers, but I.Q. doesn't seem to affect a man's ability to feel regret or his ability to reduce the dissonance he experienced. As long as the soldiers speak English well enough to understand the decision they are making, the same processes seems to exist regardless of I.Q. level.

Hoyt: That's interesting because common sense might suggest that the less intelligent the individual, the more self-doubt, the more worry he would have about whether or not he made a good decision, because, perhaps, being less intelligent, he is not accustomed to making good decisions.

Walster: That's a very good point.

Hoyt: He has learned that he has a lot to worry about in this life, and he is always, as they say, "goofing off."

Walster: Probably one reason people engage in this "rationalization" process is to make their decisions consistent in quality with their own good images of themselves. "I feel I am a good decision maker, and therefore, I am concerned that *this* decision be a good decision." You would expect both that the bright person would be more convinced that he was a good decision maker and that he could think of more ways to convince himself that any given decision had been a good one. If a fellow thought of himself as a poor decision maker, on the other hand, the kind of person who always makes the wrong decision, he is not really being consistent if he convinces himself that a given decision was a really marvelous one—the kind that he never makes. He might not feel content until he finds out what's *wrong* with it.

Hoyt: I've known, and I am sure we've all known some children who have super I.Q.'s who can make amazing, and in fact, depressingly incorrect decisions.

Walster: That's true. However, it does appear that in general, people are both bright enough to convince themselves that they made a good decision, and have enough self-assurance so that they *want* to convince themselves that they make good decisions. Regret and dissonance-reduction seem to be a pretty general process. We didn't select the army men in any way. I agree, though, that we can probably think of exceptions.

Professor Mason: Is there any reason to think the changes of preferences you described would actually affect the future conduct of the people?

Walster: Oh, yes. You'll remember that after four minutes the soldiers were said to be regretting their decisions. We wanted to know how strong this regret was. We wondered what would happen if after four minutes soldiers had a chance to take back their decisions, a chance to do it over again. Would the regret that they felt actually be strong enough to make them pick something less desirable than the alternative they would have picked to start with?

To find out, we conducted an experiment with some college girls.[2] We designed a situation in which girls were required to make a decision. Then about two or three minutes later, just when they should be feeling regret, we gave them a chance to change their minds.

Here is the procedure we followed: The girls came in and looked at pictures of ten hairstyles. And at this time, they rated the attractiveness of all ten hairstyles. At the time of this first rating, they didn't know that they were going to be given a chance to get their hair cut and set in one of the ten styles. They found that out later. Then we picked out two hairstyles the girls liked fairly much and that seemed to be right for the girl's present hair length. It was then that we divided the girls into two groups. In the first group, we asked the girls to rank the hairstyles in attractiveness. When making these rankings, the girls still didn't know that we would soon offer them a choice of having their hair cut in one of two ways. As soon as these rankings were complete, the girl was shown the two crucial styles and asked which of these two hairstyles she would like for herself. In most cases, 72 per cent of the time, the girl chose the one she had rated higher in the initial ratings.

Girls in the second group were treated a little differently. In this group, while the girls were doing the second ranking, they *were* told that soon they would be asked to choose one of two indicated styles for themselves. Then they proceeded to rank all ten styles. Well, obviously the girls are making an implicit choice while they are ranking the styles. In a two-minute pause which followed the girls' implicit decisions, regret had a chance to build up. At the end of this pause, we asked girls to make a formal decision. And as we expected, regret had occurred. Seventy per cent of the girls chose the hairstyle that they liked *less* initially. We caught them right in the regret phase when they were thinking: "What have I done?" During this period, the rejected alternative suddenly looked more attractive, in fact, attractive enough to make many girls choose it at the time of their formal decision.

Wright: I've been caught in the regret stage by waiters or waitresses. Say I had a hard time deciding between the crab meat and the beefsteak, and I finally chose the beefsteak. If, by accident, the waiter comes back and says he has forgotten my order or something, I am awfully tempted to shift. However, if he waits for a long time, I almost never change my mind. I've mustered up some self-consistency by then.

Hoyt: What this really amounts to is that you do a thing, then only later you decide that you shouldn't have done it, rather than deciding beforehand.

Walster: Probably we do both.

---

[2] Leon Festinger and Elaine Walster, "Post-Decision Regret and Decision Reversal" in Leon Festinger's *Conflict, Decision and Dissonance* (Stanford University Press, 1964).

Hoyt: The stronger decision seems to come after, so that the cause and effect are twisted around in terms of time.

Walster: We know that people are generally quite objective about evaluating information before they make their decisions. But once they have decided on a house, for example, then they don't want to hear about all of the glories of apartment living. They are looking for a different kind of information after they have made the decision.

Hoyt: Does this imply, in your judgment, that a person who has made a decision can't, subsequently, acknowledge that he has made a terrible mistake and have to live with that?

Walster: Oh, no. I'm sure people do this. One of the things that causes such disillusionment is that a person gets a wealth of information that he made the wrong choice. If you buy a house and the basement floods and a tornado blows the roof off, it's very hard to convince yourself that you made a good choice.

You can try to convince yourself that the house has other advantages, but you can only go so far. If the environmental evidence is overwhelming, you can't succeed in reducing dissonance.

Mason: It seems to me that even when the environmental evidence isn't overwhelming, it's desirable to learn to be realistic about the choice that you have made and the mistakes that you have made. This is one of the things that we try to teach people.

Wright: You know, time enters here too. If a person is trying to make a realistic choice, deciding what's in it for himself, considering if you will, his own enlightened self-interest, the timing of the events that convince him may make a very large difference.

I want to give you an example. I will try to make it as simplified a version of a scientific experiment as I can. This experiment[3] was actually conducted by a professor at the University of Pennsylvania.

Here's what the experimenter did in this experiment. He was trying to get the children to resist from choosing an attractive toy. He would begin by arranging some toys in front of the children. Now I'll just lay out these trinkets which I always carry around in my pockets in case I should meet a child. Now, I have an array of toys. The important thing about the array is that to a little girl or boy, one toy is much more attractive than the others. In each array of toys that the experimenter presented, there would be one toy which was clearly the most attractive. Then the experimenter would ask the child "which toy would you like to play with?" When the child reached for the toy that he wanted to play with, which was always the most attractive toy in the array, the experimenter would punish the child very mildly, by pushing his hand away.

The child was then told to reach for another toy. He was allowed to choose any toy except the most attractive one. The experimenter would let the child play with whichever less attractive toy he chose. When the child was done play-

---

[3] J. Aronfreed. "Internalized Behavior Suppression and the Timing of Social Punishment," *Journal of Personality and Social Psychology,* v. 1 (1965), pp. 3-16.

ing, the experimenter would take the toy back, remove the entire set of toys, bring the child five more, and go through the same procedure once again. Each time the child reached for the most attractive toy, the experimenter would gently punish him. After awhile, of course, the child began to learn that it did no good to reach for the most attractive toy in each array because the most attractive toy was forbidden by the experimenter. So, after awhile the child would forego the most attractive toy and reach for another less attractive one.

To test whether or not the child really learned to avoid the most attractive toy, the experimenter then, on a critical test trial, left the room saying to the child: "Here's a new set of five. You can play with the one you like." Then the experimenter left the child alone. Of course, the experimenter actually walked around behind the one-way mirror and observed what the child did. In this, perhaps, somewhat sneaky way, the experimenter was able to find out whether or not the child took his lesson to heart. If he had not really learned that it was 'wrong' to choose the most attractive toy, we would expect him to choose the attractive toy that he presumably wanted all along when no one was watching. If he chose one of the less attractive toys, it would indicate that he had learned that the attractive toy, in all of these games, was forbidden.

Now comes the timing part. During the training trials, the child was taught not to play with his first choice toy in one or two different ways. For one group, called the "early punishment group," the child was treated like this: After the experimenter said, "Take the toy that you would like to play with," and just *before* the child actually touched the most attractive toy, the experimenter would push the child's hand away and say, "No, you can't have that one; choose again." In what was called a "late punishment group," the experimenter would do something different. He would say: "Which toy would you like to play with?" Then, instead of punishing the child as he reached the toy, the experimenter allowed the child to pick up the toy and to play with it for a minute. Then he said: "No, you can't have that one; choose again." *When* the experimenter punished the child was the only difference between the two groups.

The results of the experiment were very clear. The children who were punished early on their way to making a mistake, were much better at resisting the temptation to play with the most attractive toy when they were alone. The inhibition of their natural preference was far stronger when they were punished *early* than when they were punished late. The explanation for this difference has a very simple psychological basis, and it goes like this: Any punishment, or threat of punishment has an inhibitory effect, a weakening effect, on the behavior that *immediately preceded it*. Punishment also causes the child to be a little bit anxious any time there is a repetition of the circumstances under which the punishment was administered. In the early punishment condition, we made the children afraid of being *tempted*. In the late punishment condition, on the other hand, the children were not made anxious until they were caught with the forbidden toy in their hands. Thus, early punishment children developed stronger restraints against picking up the most attractive toy than did late-punishment children.

Lewis: Being careful to punish a child at the right time is all right in a controlled experiment. However, when a woman has half a dozen youngsters to watch at home, it's a different situation.

Wright: I have two short of a half-dozen and there isn't much difference and I certainly would agree. The logic that I have offered you would require the mother to be ever alert and watchful and to, somehow, physically guess when her child was about to do something wrong and say "no-no," so that he would become worried about *starting* to do wrong instead of being worried about completing a wrong action. This is very hard to do, although some parents, strangely enough, can do it.

A better way of controlling behavior, probably, is to attempt to change the child's underlying attitudes—to make him want to do what is right. In the previous experiment, we said only that we get the child to leave the most attractive toy alone. But how can we get a child to *want* to leave the toy alone? Can we get at what underlies his actual behavior?

This question brings us back to this old problem of what happens after an individual makes a choice? Let's take a very hypothetical example. I'd like to talk about a hypothetical case—we'll use this cartoon sequence to describe it. Here, in the striped shirt, is a young man who sees another boy with a candy bar in his hand. Our hero thinks that the candy is attractive; he'd like it. On the other hand, he looks at the size of the other boy, who owns the candy, and decides, I guess, that discretion is the better part of valor. He ends up walking away, wishing he had the candy. In the third picture he is still thinking about it: "Gee, that was a beautiful candy bar." In his memory it is exaggerated—we've shown it extra big here, to demonstrate that the boy is thinking of it as a very attractive candy bar, perhaps as even more attractive than it really was.

Lewis: Sort of like: The grass is greener on the other side of the fence.

Wright: Right. In fact, I often call this, the "green grass" phenomenon. The grass is greener when it's unobtainable. Now, let's go back to the beginning again. Here's our boy and he's watching this older and bigger child eat a candy bar which he would like to have for himself. But now suppose, that the other boy were not older and bigger, but *smaller* and weaker and generally more vulnerable. And let's suppose, also, that our hero has no conscience; either because he's too young or because we've just suspended it for a moment. He would like to take this candy bar away from the smaller and younger boy and eat it, but the younger boy is just big enough so that he feels a little bit of hesitation. He decides not to do it. Afterward when he thinks about the incident, he is not quite sure why he let the little boy keep his candy bar. In his mind the action of not trying to get the candy for himself, is a choice he made, but it's really not justified. He can't think of any good, hard-headed, selfish reason why he shouldn't have taken the candy for himself; the kid was smaller than he. He could have gotten away with it. Why didn't he do it? This lack of justification makes him feel uncomfortable.

Well, he can't go back and reverse his behavior. But what he can do is change his beliefs or his values in a small way. What he can say to himself to make him feel his actions had more justification is, "Well, the reason I didn't do it is because it was a very small and unattractive candy bar anyway. This is what you might call "sour grapes" effect.

So we have a "green grass" effect if an object is definitely unobtainable, and a "sour grapes" effect if the object is available, but for some reason you choose not to take it.

Hoyt: But I'm still a little confused here. Your conclusion seems to be based on an amoral situation. What if he plans to go back and tell Mummy, "I have foregone this opportunity to thrash a little boy and grab his candy bar?" Then wouldn't the reverse effect possibly take place? Wouldn't he magnify the attractiveness of the candy bar—make it seem three times as large because his reward, you see, will be three times as satisfying.

Lewis: So that he's more of a martyr.

Walster: What John wants to do there is arrange a situation where there's either high justification for doing something or not doing something. If the reward that you expect at home (praise) is immense, or if your conscience is so strong that it says "No, you can't do that!" then, a person *has* high justification for what he's doing. To test John's notions, you'd have to pick a situation that doesn't have these problems.

Lewis: In the lower example, wouldn't the boy be just as apt to run home crying and ask his mother to get him a candy bar, or something?

Wright: Perhaps so. And there you're revealing that you're really in better touch with the realistic point of view of a child than I am. Why don't I describe a situation without these particular problems. I'll describe one experiment[4] that's

---

[4] E. A. Turner and J. C. Wright, "Effect of Severity of Threat and Perceived Availability on the Attractiveness of Objects," *Journal of Personality and Social Psychology,* v. 2 (1965), pp. 128-32.

been done about three times with pre-school children. In this experiment, again, toys were used and children were asked to rank-order toys. That is, they were asked, "Of this array of toys spread out across the room, which one, looking at all of them, would you like to play with most of all?" And that one was lifted out of the array and the experimenter would say, "Of all the toys that are left, which one would you like to play with most of all." This procedure went on until the child had ranked the toys from most preferred down to least-preferred.

Then, somewhere along in the middle a "middle ranked" toy was chosen by the experimenter who would say to the child, "Well, you can't play with this particular toy, but you can play with any of the rest of them." The experimenter would then leave the room. Now in this experiment, no one expected anything but compliant behavior from the children and that's what they got. None of the children played with the forbidden toy.

For one half of the children, when warning them not to play with the toy, the experimenter said something very strong in the way of a threat: "If you play with this toy, you can't play with any of the other toys again. I'll be very angry, I'll take all my toys and go home, and I won't play with you anymore. So don't play with this toy." This is a strong threat for a child, especially since it's from a stranger, and the children, of course, comply with it.

The milder threat used for the remainder of the subjects was something like this: "Well, I really would rather you didn't play with this toy. Play with the others." Then the experimenter would leave.

Now, we're not interested as we were in a previous experiment, whether the child obeys this prohibition while the experimenter is out of the room. In this experiment, all the children obeyed the prohibition, even the mild prohibition. But we were interested in how they would re-rank the toys after the whole experiment was over—immediately after, a few days after, or even thirty to forty-five days after the experiment. We found that with a strong threat ("You can't have it. I'd be very angry and take all my toys and go home if you play with that toy."), we get the "green grass" phenomenon. The forbidden toy becomes more desirable because it is unavailable. The child, after all, was in the position of saying, "Well, the man must think that the forbidden toy is pretty special or he wouldn't have put all of this emphasis on it."

On the other hand—and this is, I think, the interesting point—the mild threat had the effect of "sour grapes." I think this is because the children who refrained from playing with the desirable toy, did so for insufficient reason. No one *really* threatened them, nothing really serious would happen if they played with the toy. These children were left in the uncomfortable position of trying to justify their behavior to themselves. For insufficient reason, they'd given up something they really would sort of like to do.

Hoyt: All the children didn't do exactly what you predicted, did they? Isn't it correct to say that the generalizations or conclusions from your experiments are the result of statistics? In other words you're working out statistical probabilities of human behavior.

Wright: You say that as if they were produced by black magic!

Hoyt: No, because we've been talking about people. But, surely, one hundred children will not all react the same way, but if you get 89 of the 100 to do so then your generalization bears out.

Wright: That's right! We can do a little better than that. If we're doing the experiment for you as a demonstration and we know how it's going to come out because we've done it before, we can tell you that 89 rather than 100 per cent are going to do it and we can say 89 plus or minus how many are going to do it and give you kind of a weather man's guide to what's going to happen. This is an improvement, I think, on just a straight, "Well, most of them will do it" kind of prediction.

Hoyt: On the periphery of these experiments, Gene, isn't there a philosophical problem, at least implied, here? The problem of free will? If the social scientist, or the psychologist specifically, can predict that 89 plus or minus two human beings will do thus under such and such circumstances, how does the philosopher react to that. Of course, we don't have ten hours, I'm sorry, the problem is huge—but isn't there a question of free will involved here?

Mason: Well, talking about children, I'm sure that children have wills of their own. Whether their wills are free is another question. I try to keep my children's wills as unfree as possible. I'm sure it's true that there is a problem. It's a terribly tangled problem, though, and I'm afraid that until the psychologist will say that an individual *can't* recognize that he's made a mistake and live with it that that or an individual child who's been given a mild threat *can't* make the same evaluation. It will be difficult for the philosopher to get his wheels moving. I don't really think that the problem arises until we have a very strong statement of that sort.

Wright: I agree with our philosopher on this point. I don't think you have to settle the classical arguments of free will and determinism here because the degree of determinism we're talking about suffers generality as it gains precision. By that I mean that we can't make really sweeping statements about everything a person's going to do with any precision at all. The more tiny our prediction, the more accurate we are. For example, when the weather man predicts what will happen ten minutes from now, he can be very, very accurate. However, if he makes his prediction range a little longer, if he tries to say what will happen two months from now, he gets less accurate. Similarly, if we're predicting what a child will do with one hand in the next three seconds, given a certain set of instructions, we can be very precise, indeed, and I don't think anyone would say that we have taken away this child's will or his freedom of will.

Lewis: But to get a child to do what you want, you should always persuade them gently instead of forcing them to do what you want.

Walster: Well, another difficulty in "controlling" people's behavior, is that people can always go outside the system. For example, once your child sees that you behave with perfect consistency, and always give him just enough threat to get him to do something, he can start controlling your behavior, very easily.

Wright: I wish that were really true. However, it is certainly true that the child who learns to cry when he's hungry is in fact learning to manipulate the behavior of the mother. He's not brainwashing her; he's simply making her come, and he's very effective at it. He yells until she does and then rewards her for coming, by stopping his yelling.

157

Hoyt: Her free will is totally limited . . .

Wright: It's fun to speculate what are the potentials and the dangers of this kind of control. The most striking thing about these changes is that the ordinary man-in-the-street psychologist, any person who is an adult or a teenager, is his own psychologist. By now he's had enough experience with life and people that he's formulated some hypotheses of his own about what makes people tick. Whether they're accurate or not, he has them and he uses them every day. At least two of these we've seen tonight don't necessarily follow quite the way we thought. Remember we said that it's common sense that a man makes up his mind and then acts on the basis of his opinion. And yet, there's a sense in which he acts first, with or without an adequate opinion, and then makes up his mind that it was the correct action to take. People tend to reinforce their own decisions. Similarly, a person may say that punishment really should precede the punished action if it's to be effective.

In the same sense. So if we could think of one's behavior—one's actual deeds and actions as going along in time and parallel to them, going along in time, one's beliefs about what one ought to be doing or what one wants to do or one should do, they influence each other. Sure, sometimes, the way common sense tells us, you make up your mind and the attitude and values you have determine your behavior; this is supposed to be the logical way. But at least as often as that, you'll act because you need to act or because for some reason you just can't help acting. Or perhaps randomly you act. And only after you act, does the behavior begin to influence the attitudes that would govern that action. So it goes both ways.

Hoyt: And these attitudes keep piling on top of each other with each successive experience. With success, the attitude is reinforced. And then the person who is only partially successful perhaps has a less strong value system? Would this be a corollary?

Wright: Perhaps so, at least temporarily. You might say that such a person had a higher incentive to establish a consistent set of values, as well. And, after all, the establishment of consistency between what you think and what you do is not only a mark of maturity, but if our analysis is correct, it's an index of how comfortable you are. Because you're not comfortable when your behaviors and your beliefs don't jibe. Everyone wants to be consistent. I guess this is really the beginning and the end of our discussion in that respect.

Hoyt: Well, we all want the result to be predictable and the total general result, happiness. And so, everything contributes to the attainment of this predictable result.

Wright: I'd love to ask you what "happiness" is.

Hoyt: This is just a general term by which I mean simply the result being, in terms of the situation, one which you can live with, one which you like. It's as simple as all that.

Walster: He knows what you mean!

Hoyt: I wish we had more time to go into other aspects of timing and decision-making as well as to explore in greater depth what we have discussed.

Economics: Time Dimension

What is the role of time in population growth, business cycles, income per capita and national development?

SPEAKER: *O. H. BROWNLEE*, PROFESSOR AND CHAIRMAN OF ECO-NOMICS

COMMENTATORS: *JOHN R. BORCHERT*, PROFESSOR OF GEOGRAPHY
                           CLEMENT UDEZE (NIGERIA), GRADUATE STUDENT IN HIS-TORY

Professor Brownlee: One of the most important problems which economists have studied for a long time is population growth. The map shows the growth of population since 1650 for the five continents and Oceana. In 1650 there were approximately half a billion people in the world. In 1850 there were about 1.2 billion. One century later, in 1964, the population had increased two and a half times from what it was in 1850. The percentage increase during the last century has been as large as it was during the previous two centuries.

In North America in 1650 there were only one million people—mostly Indians, I presume. In 1850, there were 55 million; in 1940, 150 million; and in 1964, 24 years later, 211 million. Middle and South America has a start on us in population having 12 million in 1650. The number dropped slightly in the next century. Since 1940, however, the population in this region has almost doubled. It was almost 130 million then; now it is 240 million.

Europe was relatively well developed in 1650 with more than 100 million people. Its growth during the next century was relatively small by current standards. Population almost doubled between 1750 and 1850 and again between 1850 and 1940. It has increased by about 20 per cent since 1940.

The African population actually fell between 1650 and 1750. There was a very slow increase even until 1940. During the three centuries from 1650 until 1940 there was only about a 70 per cent increase in population. Like Latin America it has almost doubled in the 25 years since 1940.

In 1650, the population of Asia including China was more than 300 million. It is now almost 6 times that much. There has been a 50 per cent increase since 1940. Australia and New Zealand had a stable population for the two centuries from 1650 to 1850. Now the population is only 18 million, which is about the same as Canada.

Professor Hurwicz: The growth of population in recent decades is nothing short of spectacular. Why has this occurred? What are the causes and their implications for the future?

Brownlee: In general, we don't know much about what has occurred. Most people believe that population is like money in the bank—that it grows according to the laws of compound interest. They think of how population would grow if

WORLD POPULATION GROWTH BY CONTINENTS FROM 1650.

EUROPE and USSR

1650	103 Million
1750	144 Million
1850	274 Million
1940	579 Million
1960	641 Million

AFRICA

1650	100 Million
1750	95 Million
1850	125 Million
1940	172 Million
1960	254 Million

NORTH AMERICA

1650	1 Million
1750	1 Million
1850	26 Million
1940	144 Million
1960	199 Million

CENTRAL and SOUTH AMERICA

1650	12 Million
1750	11 Million
1850	33 Million
1940	132 Million
1960	206 Million

ASIA (excluding USSR)

1650	327 Million
1750	475 Million
1850	741 Million
1940	1,213 Million
1960	1,679 Million

OCEANIA

1650	2 Million
1750	2 Million
1850	2 Million
1940	11 Million
1960	16 Million

POPULATION

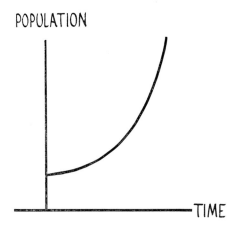

TIME

it were unconstrained and were like money in a bank which was drawing interest compounded continuously.

Hurwicz: What would be a reasonable rate of population growth?

Brownlee: A reasonable growth rate might be about two to two-and-one-half per cent for the world as a whole, which would mean that population would double approximately every 30 to 35 years.

Hurwicz: By the year 2000 then, we could have six billion more people than we have now.

Brownlee: Predictions for this magnitude are being made currently. Many people are worried that we may not have standing room by the year 2100. This concept of population growing as does our money in the bank is a fairly recent one. I believe that Malthus, an English economist, was one of the first people to formulate a systematic theory of population growth. His theory said that, in the absence of any constraint, population would grow as in the picture above. However, this is a so-called exponential or geometric growth curve. According to Malthus, the food supply grows arithmetically and when the population catches up with the food supply, population also can grow only arithmetically.

Hurwicz: That's the Malthusian theory.

Brownlee: Yes. In the 1930's we were quite worried about population not growing rapidly enough. The curve shown represents the growth of fruit flies beginning with a pair. When the jar gets full, approximately, the fly population is at the line labeled "maximum." A number of population theorists believed that this kind of curve accurately describes population behavior for humans. Just why this was the case unless we can be thought to have some kind of constraint, such as food supply, which acts in the same fashion as reaching the top of the bottle does for fruit flies, I cannot say. However, during the 1930's many people believed we were rapidly approaching the maximum—a stationary population— and some countries, including Germany and France, were subsidizing population

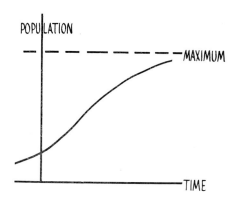

growth. Some economic theorists in the United States believe that the depression was actually related to the rate of growth of population and that one way to get out of the depression was to speed population growth.

I had considered introducing a picture of what has been happening to the food supply, but I find that the food supply concept is an ambiguous one. If we measure it in tons, it becomes quite hard to compare tons of watermelon with tons of dried milk. Even calories are not a very good measure. In particular, diets have improved so that the percentage of calories which comes from solely carbohydrate sources is much smaller now than it was.

One indicator of the growth of potential food supply is the percentage of population engaged in agriculture. There has been a marked decline in almost all countries of the world over the last 20 to 25 years. In the United States, with its food surplus, 10 per cent of the population is now engaged in agricultural production; and this percentage continues to fall. The Soviet Union has less than 50 per cent of its population engaged in agriculture. It wasn't too long ago that 85 per cent or 90 per cent of the population was engaged in growing the food supply necessary to support the entire population.

Our current theories about population are best described by the first diagram. At the moment we're not worried so much about food constraints as we are about space constraints.

Hurwicz: In fact, during the 1930's when there was some stability of population in countries such as France, this stability was not due to a shortage of food. There were sociological factors of one sort or another.

Brownlee: This now seems to be the case.

At that time people believed that as income rose, population growth fell, and they, therefore, expected that the population growth rates in the poorer countries, those of Latin America and Africa, would also fall off as their incomes approached the levels which had been achieved by France and Germany in the 1930's. We now find that the rich countries as well as the poor ones have high population rates. India has a high population growth rate; the net growth rates in some of Latin America are on the order of three per cent. Even population growth rate in the United States was more than two per cent in the period from 1940 to

1955. The theory that there is a relation between income and population growth is not a very good one. There must be other factors.

Professor Borchert: I gather from what you were saying before about the food supply that there may well be a maximum amount of food that can be produced. Nobody knows for sure what this maximum is and doesn't it change continually?

Brownlee: With current technology and existing population, land, and so on, there is probably some maximum amount of food that could be produced and maximum population which could be supported if we devoted ourselves entirely to food production. However, this is a very large number. Remember that an important factor in growth of the food supply during the last 25 years has been the improvement in agricultural technology. We have no reason to expect that it would continue to improve at the same rate that it has since 1935, although improvement has not yet ceased.

Hurwicz: Suppose that technology were to remain roughly what it is now, and that the amount of food that is available at present is inadequate if the population were to double in 30 years, there really is no obvious place where we could get twice as much wheat as is now being grown.

Brownlee: We could probably get twice as much wheat as is now being produced. However, if population were to double and there were to be no change in food supply—whatever this may mean—I would guess that there would be notable changes in the composition of the food supply. We might get considerably less from livestock products which require relatively large amounts of resources per nutritive unit and get more from vegetable sources of protein and carbohydrates. The diet of the Chinese, in comparison with the diets of the Western Europeans or Americans, contains a significantly larger portion of protein from fish and vegetable sources.

Another kind of problem in which economists are interested is the relationship between income and time. We have a representation of manufacturing production and real gross national product (GNP) in the United States from 1866 to 1956.[1] Notice that in addition to the general upward movement which is fairly marked—probably at the rate of something like two-and-a-half to three per cent per year—there are quite a few ups and downs. The biggest decline occurred between 1930 and 1932, but there are others in 1873, 1921 and 1948. These ups and downs are referred to by some people as business cycles.

Although we have many theories which try to explain these ups and downs or the so-called *cyclical* movement in economic activity, economists have tended to draw upon mechanics for theories to explain such cycles. The chart shows how economic activity might move over time if it were described by a mechanical theory. Notice that the distance between the peaks is always the same; also, the distance between the troughs or the bottom points are the same. This is a cycle with a regular period, and its amplitude is constant.

Borchert: It means that history ought to repeat itself.

---

[1] B. G. Hickman, "Postwar Cyclical Experience and Economic Instability," *American Economic Review*, vol. 48, May, 1958, p. 122.

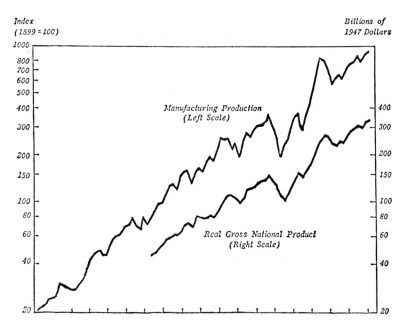

Manufacturing Production and Gross National Product, 1866-1956.

Brownlee: History exactly repeats itself except for the growth portion. However, it's possible to get something that looks like a cycle even though there's no underlying cyclical mechanism. I have taken some numbers drawn at random and added them to a general movement which would be not cyclical and we have a picture that's not unlike the one showing the movement of manufacturing production or the gross national product over time. A high point is followed by a low point which is followed by another high point . . . One could smooth this and make it look something like the sine or cosine curve which gives a regular cycle.

Borchert: It should be rather encouraging to us when we lose on the stock market to know that it perhaps is just chance and not our stupidity. That also applies when we gain on the stock market.

Brownlee: As far as the stock market is concerned, apparently there are no good predictors.

Borchert: That's true, too, of the real estate market.

Brownlee: Studies of the stock market show that if you bought a bundle of stock, chosen at random rather than by some selecting device, you'd do approximately as well as the concerns which buy bundles of stock. However, I'm showing this simply to indicate that we can see cycles where they really don't exist.

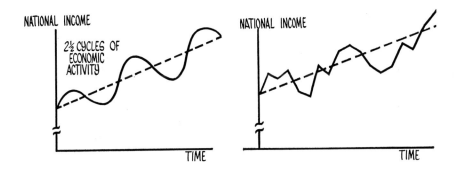

Mr. Udeze: What is the relation between population, national income, and the possible business cycles? Are you saying that population is the cause of these business cycles or national income or what?

Brownlee: Population probably doesn't have very much to do with business cycles. I'm not a believer in the business cycle as such. My explanation of what we observe is that it's a result of unexplained phenomena—the random terms which I've added here to get the picture which shows numbers picked at random to make a cycle. Population, however, certainly does have something to do with the growth of national income. As long as people are productive, the total output from more people should be greater than the total output from fewer. Estimates which have been made for Western Europe and for the United States indicate that if you increase population by one per cent, you'll increase production by about 0.7 per cent. Clearly, however, if there were no changes other than increased population, income per capita (income divided by the number of people) would fall.

Economists are interested in per capita income as a measure of the welfare of a particular group of people. Not everyone likes this preoccupation with per capita income. At the moment, quite a few people consider income per capita as a relatively decent measure of economic welfare. In this sense there's a link between national income and population.

Udeze: I have a question about business cycles. This pattern is supposed to be the trend of business cycles in the developed countries of the world. Do business cycles occur also in the underdeveloped areas and, if so, what are the causes?

Brownlee: Income in any country doesn't move up in a smooth fashion. Usually there are differing year to year or quarter to quarter fluctuations. What's responsible for these things? In the United States there are some people who claim that our movement of income upward would have been smoother, and perhaps even faster, if we hadn't tried to speed up the economy at some times and then slow it down at other times.

Perhaps a better example of this deliberate manipulation would be Japan or Great Britain. What Great Britain has been doing, in response to its balance of payments problem, is to try to cut down on its imports through cutting its income. Its so-called "stop and go" policy—slowing the economy down when its balance of payments is unfavorable and speeding it up when its balance of payments is more favorable—would lead to definitely differing rates of change in income.

My guess, however, is that the things which cause observed values to change at an irregular rate in the United States or in Great Britain might be quite different from those that cause fluctuations in Nigeria or Colombia. In particular, an underdeveloped country which relies to a large extent upon production of raw materials for its income will be subject to price fluctuations in these raw materials. These fluctuations are somewhat larger than in manufactured goods and might, therefore, be responsible for a considerable amount of the irregular movement.

Hurwicz: Isn't it true that people in this country, at one time at least, felt that we had sectors of the economy which were somewhat in the same position as the underdeveloped countries have been? For example, the agricultural sector before price stabilization policies went into effect was subject to tremendous price fluctuations, as are underdeveloped economies now.

Brownlee: That's right. We would find that the variation in the income of North Dakota would be larger than the variation in the income of Washington, D.C., because variations in crop yields and fluctuations in prices both would enter into the determination of fluctuations of income in North Dakota, whereas there isn't very much in the way of agriculture which would enter into the income of Washington, D.C.

Borchert: Well, how does an underdeveloped economy become developed? How do you know when it's becoming developed? What are the symptoms?

Brownlee: I think the line between development and underdevelopment is purely an income line. We arbitrarily say that if income per capita is greater than a certain number, the country is called a developed country. If it's smaller than a certain amount, but larger than another particular amount, it's called a semi-developed country. If it's smaller than a certain income, it's called an underdeveloped country. If a country's income per capita is $500 or less it might be considered underdeveloped; if it's between $500 and $800, semi-developed. If it's more than $800, developed.

I'm not sure exactly what the dividing lines are, but they are something like the ones we're using here. A country is developed when its income gets large enough. How it gets developed is another question. I've already mentioned the fact that income grows as population grows and that there is about 0.7 per cent growth in income for each one per cent growth in population. Growth in income is also the result of growth in the capital stock. There are more machines, more roads, more buildings, more houses, now than there were 30 years ago or 100 years ago.

Borchert: Is this 0.7 per cent growth in income per capita or total?

Brownlee: It is total. The per capita income would fall as the population grows—if the growth were due only to population change. A rough figure for the productivity of capital is about 0.3 per cent increase in output for each 1 per cent increase in the amount of capital. We're adding capital at the rate of 3 or 4 per cent a year, and if this were all we'd get about a 0.9 to 1.2 per cent increase in income per year, which is slow. The other three-fourths of the annual income increases due to what we call technological change. If we just kept our resources constant—had neither more capital nor more population—we would also get more product, because we know how to produce better today than we did 40 years ago.

The most dramatic illustration of this is in the field of agriculture. With the same land and less population—fewer people on farms—we're producing more of nearly everything now than we did in 1940. This has been due largely to the improvement in varieties of crops, breeds of livestock, and feeding and growing methods. We're able to convert feed into poultry and livestock products much more efficiently than we were able to before.

Hurwicz: Is there also some capital accumulation in this?

Brownlee: In many respects it's rather difficult to separate technological change from capital accumulation. Some people argue that the increase in per capita income is due, among other things, to the improvement in the educational level. Yet it's hard to show educational levels in the same way as we show new roads, new dams, and so forth. The populations of underdeveloped countries like to see tangible evidence of growth. They like to see greater investment in education, but the things which seem most impressive to them are dams, roads, and other more tangible improvements.

Borchert: How about steel mills?

Brownlee: Yes, steel mills and airlines are impressive. A master's degree in history won't be quite as impressive as a $100,000 factory even though the productivities of each might be approximately the same.

Borchert: It sounds to me as though they have about the same values as we do.

Brownlee: Do you mean that a master's degree in history doesn't look as good as an airline in this country?

We don't know very much about what causes economic growth. A lot of people have said that what we need to do in order to get growth is to increase the ratio of capital to output. Actually, we find that the capital-output ratio in the United States has been falling rather consistently over the last three or four decades. If we take countries where growth rates have been small, some of them—Argentina, for example—have a rather large capital-output ratio in comparison with the United States.

West Germany and Japan have relatively small capital-output ratios. Taking a simple number such as the ratio of our capital stock to our population and saying that economic growth is described by this or can be cured by changes in this certainly oversimplifies the problem. Let me say at this point that economists don't lack theories for explaining all these things—population, business cycles, or economic growth. Our trouble is that we have too many theories. There were something like 40 business cycle theories in existence before 1942, all of which seemed equally plausible in explaining the cycle, but none of which actually would have been useful for prediction purposes.

Hurwicz: Is this because we in economics are not able to do an experiment which would tell us which of those theories was right?

Brownlee: Well, in a sense, I think this is true. We're not in a position to replicate things in the same fashion as a physicist, a chemist or a biologist. We try to obtain observations that are, in a sense, comparable to what the physicist or the chemist obtains by analyzing the movements of things over time. Our problem here is that the number of observations which we have is really rather small. We can't have much confidence with about 50 years of data relative to such things as income, capital stock, number of years of education, and so on.

Borchert: Does the evolution of history itself plague you at all? You simply can't reproduce the conditions in the United States at the end of the Civil War for purposes of analysis.

Brownlee: Perhaps these conditions are being reproduced in some other country which has a per capita income about the size of ours during the Civil War. However, the reproduction cannot be completely accurate since neither the airplane nor the atomic bomb existed in 1860. Many people believe that we can get some important insights about how underdeveloped countries might grow by studying the economic histories of those countries which have already had successful growths. I'm not confident that this is going to be very useful. I'm reminded of Professor Hurwicz's description of a comparable method of weather forecasting which perhaps he'd like to relate to us. There is a lesson to be learned here for those who want to look at developed countries a hundred years ago to see how their growth took place and then try to make projections from this for growth of currently underdeveloped countries.

Hurwicz: The technique that you are referring to actually was tried some 20 to 25 years ago. The idea was to accumulate data concerning weather history for about 50 years or so and then try to find one or two days in that past period that would be very much like today and yesterday. If you could find those two days, say, ten years ago that were exactly like today and yesterday in Minneapolis, you might hope that tomorrow would be like the third day ten years ago. As it turned out, one of the main obstacles was not so much any lack of logic in this technique, but the fact that it's very hard to get a sequence of days in the past that will be really like what you have now if you look accurately enough. By and large weather remains similar over decades, though it is not without change. For instance, the climate might change. In any case, there is probably more stability than in economics. I don't know if you would quite agree with that.

Borchert: Wouldn't you be describing the economist's problem, Leo, if you added to this, a continuous, irregular but significant change, say, in the composition of the atmosphere from year to year?

Hurwicz: For instance, if nuclear tests really have changed the climate, you'd be living in a new climatic era.

Brownlee: The weather people have an advantage over us—they have a lot more observations. We have, in effect, 50 days of weather maps to look at, since our useful data for many purposes run back to about 1919, the end of World War I. We usually have to throw out the four or five years during the Second World War. So, we have about 42 "days of weather" to look at.

Hurwicz: You are calling a year " a day".

Brownlee: Unlike weather, in economics we can be pretty sure that tomorrow will be pretty much like today. If we looked at the gross national product on five consecutive days, we'd find there that there was little variation in it, except in cases where there was a big strike or a holiday. Therefore, we have to add quite a few of these days together in order to get so-called independent observations. A year might be considered a minimal period for independence, in which case we have but only 46 weather days more or less.

Udeze: Since you are talking about economic growth, I would like to ask you a question that bothers many of us, especially in the underdeveloped areas. We hear economists and politicians talk about "bridging the gap" between the high and the low, between the wealthy and the less wealthy nations. Yet, we find out that the rate of growth in the developed countries is greater than in the underdeveloped. Can we accomplish this "bridging the gap," or is it getting wider and wider?

Brownlee: First of all, the growth rates among countries differ widely. There are some developed countries which have been growing rather slowly and some which have been growing rapidly, as some underdeveloped countries which have been growing slowly and others which have been growing rapidly. Even if the growth rates were the same, of course, a country which started from a lower income base than another one would find that the absolute difference between its income and that of the richer country would widen. If Nigeria, for instance, started from $100 a year and the United States started from a thousand dollars per year and both countries double their incomes in the same period of time, Nigeria will end up with $200 and the United States will end up with $2,000. They were $900 apart at the start and $1,800 apart at the end.

I think that the absolute differences between the incomes in the underdeveloped countries and the incomes in the developed countries are widening. What can be done about it? This is a much more difficult question. We in the United States feel guilty about it. We're trying to give some of our income away, but our gifts are on a pretty small scale. We're giving away something on the order of four billion dollars a year, and quite a bit of this is material that people can't use to increase their incomes—namely, military equipment.

Hurwicz: They can use it profitably but not in a way that is going to influence per capita income.

Brownlee: It doesn't help their incomes very much.

Udeze: Do economists visualize a time when all nations will be self-sufficient? If there will be such a time, what will you think of economic activity?

Brownlee: I hope that they would not necessarily be self-sufficient.

Hurwicz: Shouldn't we clarify this? Mr. Udeze, when you talk about an economy, such as Nigeria, being self-sufficient, do you mean that it wouldn't have to trade with any other country? Or do you just mean that it would be able to exist economically on its own without being aided from outside?

Udeze: I think I imply both.

Hurwicz: These are two somewhat different things.

Brownlee: Great Britain, for example, is not self-sufficient in the first sense. It exports and imports a lot and survived very well until the last election, at least.

Borchert: Wouldn't it be fair to say that the trends of the last two or three centuries, in particular the last century and a half, have been running strongly in the direction away from self-sufficiency in the first sense of the word?

Brownlee: Again, there has been a kind of cyclical movement here. The period between 1919 and 1939 was a period in which there was contraction, relatively speaking, of world trade. The contraction was particularly sharp between 1929 and 1939.

Hurwicz: Of course, tremendous restrictions were developed—exchange controls, and high tariffs, and so on.

Brownlee: Since the end of World War II, there has been an expansion in trade. Certainly there has been an expansion in absolute terms. Whether there's been an expansion in the percentage of production which is exported I cannot say. Such data are available, but I'm not familiar with them.

Borchert: It might be significant to look at the really great industrialization that has taken place in Northwestern Europe and the United States and the Soviet Union. It seems to me you can associate this with the embracing of very greatly expanded geographical areas from which these industrial and urban population concentrations were able to draw their resources. In other words, they were actually establishing exchange economies over greatly expanded areas during the process of this economic growth.

Brownlee: Your answer to Mr. Udeze's question would be that you don't want self-sufficiency in the sense of not exporting or importing. This certainly would be my answer also. Nigeria should not have its own airline, its own steel mill, its own auto manufacturing plants, or grow all of its own wheat and meat. It could expand its income considerably by international trade.

Hurwicz: I think that Dean Borchert's point went a little beyond this, although this was part of it. What he was also saying, if we were to apply it to the context of Africa, was that perhaps the best chance they will have for development would be to create some kind of unity over the whole continent or a very large portion of it so that they could draw on mineral resources, agricultural resources, and the reservoir of manpower without having to cross frontiers every time and be stopped by bureaucratic controls.

Brownlee: That would help, providing that they didn't also shut out trade from the outside. A customs union, for example, can be beneficial providing that you don't, at the same time, constrain too much the trade between countries that are not in the union and those that are.

Hurwicz: Didn't the United States discourage foreign trade in the nineteenth century while depending on its big internal area for economic growth?

Brownlee: Yes, it did, but it might have grown even more rapidly if it had not discouraged trade.

Hurwicz: Americans at that time believed the opposite.

Brownlee: Perhaps we'll never know who was correct.

Borchert: The Russians apparently believe the same thing now.

Brownlee: Yet they're trying to expand trade.

Let's get back to Mr. Udeze's question. Let's talk about self-sufficiency in another sense, that of standing on your own feet without having to receive aid from richer countries. If there were no constraints to people moving from one country to another, if people really looked at the size of per capita income in deciding where to live, and if the education and skill levels were the same in Nigeria as they were in the United States, then we'd expect per capita incomes to be approximately the same. There's not free movement of population and we look for substitutes which will tend to equalize income.

Economists have shown that, under very special conditions (which don't exist), trading between countries is a good substitute for moving population. That is, you could equalize per capita income just by trade if these conditions existed. Although the conditions needed for equalization to occur don't actually exist, there's certainly a tendency toward equalization that results from trade.

Another thing that could be done is to move the capital to the people. This, of course, is what the United States and Western Europe are trying to do, although it is on a very small scale, through such things as the various international loan programs. The Alliance for Progress is a device for, among other things, trying to speed up the growth of capital in Latin America through private loans as well as public ones.

One might ask the question, "Why doesn't the capital move into these countries, particularly when the rates of return seem to be high?" Obviously, political factors are important. You may be able to earn 25 per cent per year on your capital, but if you have had it for only a couple of years the government may take it over. A climate that really attracts private investment is one thing that helps to increase the incomes of underdeveloped countries. Increased education is another means for increasing per capita income.

Hurwicz: Professor Brownlee, you were saying earlier that our knowledge of causation of economic phenomena is quite limited. Nevertheless, I think economists do get called upon to advise a variety of clients including countries that want to undertake a program of development. Haven't you sometimes been in a position of having to answer questions about this? What can we tell developing countries or countries that want to work out a rational method for economic development? Supposing the government of Nigeria asked you for suggestions along those lines, what would you say?

Brownlee: There are some pretty obvious things that we can tell them. First of all, while the forecasting record of economists is not very good, in fact it is rather miserable, there is still a section of economics that abstracts from time and which I think has really quite a bit to say. This kind of economics is called "economic statics" and deals with problems of resource allocation or "how to do things the easy way."

It has something useful to say to underdeveloped countries. For example, it tells us not to put up a steel mill in Nigeria. It would be much more productive for Nigeria to devotes its resources to producing things other than steel and then trade these things for steel. It's probably also not desirable to have a Nigerian National Airline.

Borchert: Why do you make such a statement, your picking on steel mills and airlines, for example? What sorts of things are you basing this on?

Brownlee: These are prestige items which most underdeveloped countries want without reference to their productivities. The minimum amount of capital which is required to set up a steel mill is something like 150 or 200 million dollars. Let's look at what the steel costs in terms of the other opportunities that have to be sacrificed. If the capital were made available at no interest cost, steel production costs probably would be about the same as the price of imported steel. However, 150 or 200 million dollars would produce an income in an underdeveloped country of somewhat between 30 and 50 million dollars per year, i.e., the rate of return on capital used in the most productive way is somewhere between 20 and 25 per cent. This is lost when the capital is sunk into the steel mill.

Hurwicz: You are not implying that they shouldn't industrialize?

Brownlee: No, I'm not implying that they shouldn't industrialize. Not at all. In general, however, they should industrialize in ways which require a relatively high ratio of labor to capital. They have a lot of labor, relatively speaking, and not very much capital. They ought to produce things which use a great deal of labor and not so much capital. They ought to use methods of production for whatever they produce which require quite a considerable amount of labor and not so much capital. We have introduced so-called labor saving devices in the United States because the price of labor is relatively high and the price of capital is relatively low. Underdeveloped countries should not try to use the same kinds of techniques, because capital is probably four times as expensive in an under-developed country as it is in the United States and labor is probably one-sixth as expensive. As a rough approximation, they might be using methods of production which use 24 times as much labor relative to capital as ours do.

Udeze: I see what you've emphasized what investment in steel would do to the country. In the context of economic growth, though, wouldn't a steel industry move the nation to greater economic activity than would, for example, a tomato factory or something of that type?

Brownlee: I think that a tomato canning factory, providing that tomatoes can be grown rather successfully in Nigeria, might be a much better thing for you to undertake than a steel mill.

Udeze: Consider that the people still need steel.

Brownlee: That's true, but they can buy steel; they can trade tomatoes for steel.

Udeze: What about the amount they pay for this imported steel? Would you encourage going ahead with a factory built on capital from foreign investors?

Brownlee: You mean, would I encourage an American investor to build a steel mill in Nigeria?

Udeze: Suppose it was in the form of loan to the government of the country, for example.

Brownlee: If an international agency asked me, "Would you okay a loan for a steel mill in Nigeria," I would probably say no.

Hurwicz: I think it is not because you want to be unpleasant to Nigerians, but because you feel in a sense that they would be wasting their own resources.

Brownlee: I'd be quite willing to make loans to Nigeria, but not for this purpose, because I want the capital which goes to Nigeria to bring the Nigerians the largest amount of income and they won't get it from a steel mill.

Borchert: Perhaps the tomato canning industry would become so large that they would have a really tremendous need for tin plate.

Brownlee: Still they can trade tomatoes for tin cans.

Hurwicz: Let me raise a point that occurs to me in connection with just this discussion. Let's say that Nigeria will take your advice, Professor Brownlee, and they will try to develop those industries that require, relatively speaking, less capital. Still, undoubtedly, they will need additional capital and, while part of it might come from abroad, they probably should expect to do a good part of their accumulation and saving by themselves. This is especially true if you think not of Nigeria, but of a country like India where the problem is of much greater magnitude. Now, how do you see the question of organizing this capital accumulation? That is, do you feel that there is a way of accomplishing this on a purely spontaneous, individual basis?

Brownlee: Well, first of all, I don't think that the bulk of the capital could come from internal sources. Let me now contradict myself and say we might have something to learn from United States experience in this case.

Hurwicz: I knew you would admit that sooner or later.

Brownlee: The United States was a very heavy importer of capital up until 1914 because the productivity of capital in this country was relatively higher than it was in Europe. We had a relatively stable political situation so that ex-propriation wasn't threatened. Europeans were willing to make investments here. The same thing ought to take place in India or Nigeria or most any other under-developed country. A saving rate of 20 per cent is a very high one.

Hurwicz: I think most of us find that to be so.

Brownlee: The saving rate of the United States is about 10 per cent. Twenty per cent of 100 dollars is $20 per capita and even with India's large population, they are not going to accumulate very much in the way of capital from their own savings.

Udeze: In connection with development of industries in the underdeveloped countries, how much do you think that the government will go into developing public utilities, telephones, and building of bridges and roads?

Brownlee: They already have gone in to it to quite a great extent. I don't know that I'd put telephones in the same category as bridges. If the roads are strategically placed they can be highly productive.

Udeze: Would you recommend that they be developed by the government or by some private group?

Brownlee: It's pretty hard for a private group to collect for the use of a road in a place like Nigeria.

Hurwicz: Hopefully, we understand the questions better than we did somewhat earlier, but I don't think that we necessarily have more answers. We have seen that time enters into the field of economics in several ways. One of them has been, of course, that economy develops through time, and another is that there are cycles of thought among economists. Things that they believed 100 years ago were known to be wrong 50 years ago, but now perhaps again turn out to be true. Perhaps that's what makes it interesting.

Time and the Significance of Politics

What significance and meaning do politics have in human destiny?

SPEAKER: *MULFORD Q. SIBLEY*, professor of political science

COMMENTATORS: *FRANK ADAMS*, state senator

                        WAYNE G. POPHAM, state senator

Professor Hoyt: If we were living twenty-three hundred years ago in Greece rather than in midwestern United States in the mid-twentieth century, the chances are exceedingly great that we would be living in a city-state, what the Greeks called a "polis." The life we would lead would be described by our contemporaries of twenty-three hundred years ago as "political" because it was the life of the polis. By that term "political" they would mean the whole life of the whole community, not just what we call politics, but the economic, the social, the spiritual and religious, and the other aspects of a community life. Aristotle, writing about that time, defined man as a political animal and I'm sure that he had in mind this broader concept of politics than we have today. However, man, in addition to being political in the Aristotelian sense, is very political in our modern and more narrow sense. Mulford, I wonder if this has always been so or how long it had been so when Aristotle first defined man as a political animal.

Professor Sibley: Well, I'm very happy that you began with Aristotle because it leads me to make a few observations about the meaning of politics and the relatively brief period during which man has experienced what we call politics. Man's pre-political experience includes roughly 94 thousand years out of 100 thousand years. It begins with the cave man, moves on up to the tribe, and ends up with the medicine man, an important figure in the tribe. Down to this point, social order was sustained by unconscious and rigid folkways, magic, or irrational force. Only in the last six thousand years, which could be noted with the figure of a certain well-known leader [President Lyndon Johnson] illustrating it, will you have what I call the political period of man's history. We cite Isaiah 1:18 "Let us reason together" because this particular figure is very fond of that passage from the Bible.

This leads me to define, tentatively, what we mean by "politics." I should say politics is that aspect of human activity in which we consciously make, implement, and evaluate policy for the collective, or for the community. Political decisions involve deliberation and aspire to rationality. That's a fairly broad definition. I think it would agree pretty well with what Professor Hoyt said about Aristotle, but I'd like to emphasize here that our political experience as such has been very, very brief in comparison with the total span of the human race on earth.

Hoyt: Politics, so defined, is an enormous subject. Mulford, would you indicate briefly the main topics that you will deal with out of the many, many that we could discuss?

MAN VS. TIME

Sibley: I'd like briefly to comment on each of the seven main topics.

1. TIME AS A SCARCE GOOD.

First of all, of course, politics is related to time in the sense that time is a scarce good, like material goods. It's an economic good, and therefore has to be allocated; it's always scarce and as a scarce good becomes part of the "stuff" of politics. Presumably, the angels do not have politics because they do not live in an arena of scarce goods. They live in the timeless realm. However, the legislature of Minnesota, for example, is always pressed for time.

2. TIME AND PREDICTION.

Time is also related, of course, to the problem of prediction. Every policy of a collective or of a community has to be based upon some sort of prediction as to where it's likely to go. Now this prediction can be for the short run or the long run and one of the real problems is to relate the short run prediction to the long prediction. Thus, for example, automation, we're told, while it will lead to short run unemployment, in the long run will not lead to unemployment. Yet Lord Keynes pointed out a good many years ago that in the long run we're all dead. What happens to those people who are thrown out of work in the short run and who don't have time to live for the long run? This problem of long run and short run in evaluating political decisions is very important.

3. TIME AND INTENSITY OF SOCIAL CHANGE.

A third great point is that time today is packed full of more social change than ever before in man's history and we're finding it very difficult to adjust to this rapidity and intensity of change. Someone has suggested that there's more change now in ten days than there used to be in ten years. This ought to be one of our themes in talking about politics.

4. TIME AND "LEGISLATION BY ACCIDENT."

Fourthly, then, Plato used to say that if we don't legislate consciously and deliberately, then events or force will legislate for us. We don't escape legislation, in other words, simply by refusing to act. I think a good illustration is the sorry mess New York City is in—I won't mention the Twin Cities—in terms of urban planning. A recent article in the *U.S. News and World Report* suggests that New York City is impossible to govern today. One of the reasons it's impossible to govern is because there was not deliberate legislation in time. The result was that events, forces, circumstances took over and legislated for them. So now it has become almost impossible to legislate consciously and deliberately. We have juvenile delinquency, crime in the streets, and all the other things we think of in connection with a big city.

5. TIME IN THE EVOLUTION OF POLITICS.

The fifth point is that time is necessary for the evolution of politics. Politics presumably doesn't exist for itself; it has to be seen in the larger perspective of man's morality, his purpose, his goals. It's interesting that many political thinkers have thought of human evolution in terms of a three-fold division. First, there is a primitive pre-political division in which social order is a matter of wont, custom, force, or magic, rather than of deliberation. Some see this period also as communist. Secondly, we have a political division which is roughly the equivalent of what we call human history. During this we gain civilization but we lose a great many things, too, because we develop class stratification; we separate human beings from one another through division of labor, and so on. The problem, then, for these thinkers becomes one of how to get the benefits of a true community with the benefits of civilization which often tends to destroy community. Therefore, many thinkers have postulated a third stage of evolution in which you combine the two. The Marxists do this, for example. Even St. Thomas Aquinas does it except that he postpones it to heaven, whereas the Marxists assume it's going to take place on earth. This is an important aspect of the way we view the political process. You might say that the political process in history, from this point of view, is one whereby we hope to gain the third stage.

6. TIME AND ASSESSMENTS OF LEGITIMACY.

Sixthly, I note on our list of problems, assessments of legitimacy. That's a long expression for saying, "What makes a government legitimate? What makes it morally right or legal?" These questions take on unusual importance when we remember that almost every government has originated in force and violence, including the United States government. Whatever the answer to that important question, we know that in fact men tend to legitimate a government if it's in office long enough, no matter how it started. Thus, William the Conqueror, who was at first regarded by most men as a terribly illegitimate ruler, became legitimate after four or five generations simply through the passage of time. Well now, is it right for time to confer legitimacy? Why does it do so in human imagination?

7. TIME AND PERSPECTIVE IN EVENTS.

Finally, just a very brief comment, the things that seem important now in politics may not seem significant in the future. Time has a way of changing our assessment of political events, doesn't it? Look back on the War of the Spanish Succession, for example. It was regarded as a life and death struggle in the 18th century. How do we view it today? Most people don't even know about it. Let's take the Taconite Amendment. Many of us became heated about it in the last election here. I wonder how our descendants will view it 100 years from now? So you can go right down the line and point out the importance of the time element in the way we look at political events. Well, I think I've commented enough on these points.

Senator Adams: Mulford, I would like to get back to the time element as a scarce commodity. We have just concluded the legislative session here and I have in my hand the Saturday session from the *Senate Journal,* the Saturday which was the last day in which we could pass bills in the Senate. I made a count of the number of bills that were passed in that last session of the legislature and there were nine hundred and some bills. On Friday, May 21, the next-to-the-last day that we could pass bills, we had passed 107 bills or about 12 per cent of the total number of bills that were passed in the whole session. During the last two days, there were 167 roll-call votes. Now, time is an element here, and an important one. Of course, not all the roll-call votes were on major pieces of legislation. There is always local legislation that's passed, such as raising the County Commissioner's or the County Attorney's salary in some small community. Nevertheless, this final session had a good deal of the meat of the legislature. Many of the appropriations bills and tax levy bills were passed in the final few days of the session. I am wondering whether we can deliberate under this pressure for adjournment, whether we can do as good a job as if we had more time.

Hoyt: Frank, doesn't a certain amount of the deliberation, which Mulford was emphasizing as essential in a political system, go on in committee before it goes to a full session of either house?

Adams: This is true. Nevertheless, discussion takes place on the floor of the Senate where you debate the bill as it comes out from the committee. We operate under a committee structure, but nevertheless, the Senate as a whole has a chance to discuss and debate . . .

Hoyt: And there's not much chance to do that when you're doing a hundred bills a day.

Adams: There is not when you're passing a hundred bills a day.

Hoyt: We elect two hundred men to the legislature, but then eight or twelve, or whatever number there are on a committee, actually do most of the deliberation on any one particular bill.

Senator Popham: Well, Frank, you don't want to give the impression that in about eight days, we could do all of the work of the session. I think we'd give people the wrong impression here. Actually, of course, most of the bills that were formally voted on were heard, perhaps, several weeks earlier in committee and had been the subject of extensive discussion.

Sibley: Wayne, may I ask you a question at this point? Isn't it true that even though only the committee has gone over a bill, ostensibly at least, the House knows what's in it and knows its implications before it passes the bill? Doesn't this all involve an enormous amount of time?

Popham: It does, Mulford, and this point of scarcity of time is something that is peculiarly appropriate in a discussion of the legislature. As Frank and I have both discovered, the scarcity of time compels, in effect, a division of labor in the legislature and necessarily results in a reliance amongst the different numbers of the body upon one another as specialists.

Sibley: That raises the interesting question of whether we really ought not have more legislative sessions.

Adams: Mulford, if you're referring to an annual session of the legislature, I would not agree with you.

Sibley: You mean you prefer undeliberate legislation, Frank?

Adams: No.

Sibley: Well, what would you do about it then?

Adams: It's just a question of time. The basic issue is a matter of economics. I think that many of the legislators would like to spend more time, but it's a question of what can they afford in terms of economics. With the salary that the average legislator gets, he just can't afford to stay in session too long.

Sibley: Well, then, we need a really fundamental change in the structure of the legislature, don't we?

Adams: I would agree with you.

Sibley: Are you going to campaign for it?

Adams: Well, getting down to specifics, campaign for what, Mulford?

Sibley: I mean a unicameral legislature which doesn't have any limitation on length of its sessions. We don't limit Congress in its sessions.

Hoyt: Isn't the issue here not only what the individual legislator can afford, but also what the State of Minnesota can afford? It's going to be a much more expensive legislature if it meets more frequently.

Sibley: Let me turn the question around. What can it afford *not* to do? It can't afford going on lagging behind the necessities for reordering the state. In terms of taxation, for example, the legislature never comes to grips with taxation in a fundamental sense. It always engages in temporizing acts, in short-run expediency.

Popham: Mulford, I think that the scarcity of time and the cost of the legislature relate not only to the members of the legislature, but also to the public. One of the ways in which scarcity of time bears upon the legislative process is the fact that it takes time for the public to get acquainted with the issues and the policies that are to be made and to communicate their views in one way or another to the members of the legislature. So the scarcity of time in our policy making process affects the public as well as the members of the legislative body.

Adams: I agree also. I think that sometimes many legislators hope that, if we can delay action on a particular problem, that somehow it will be swept under the rug and we won't have to be faced with resolving the problem. These are very controversial and it's sometimes easier to sweep them under the rug than to come to grips with them. You were talking about taxes. Your point is true; it's easier to delay than to come out forthrightly for a particular program. Now, you were asking me a minute ago about my feelings about a unicameral legislature. I doubt very much whether this thing can become an accomplished fact. The only place where we have a unicameral legislature is in Nebraska and the only way that it got to be an accomplished fact in Nebraska was that Senator Norris was instrumental with a petition and a referendum. They had to have about 100,000 signatures, and then they put it on a ballot. We don't have that provision in our State Constitution so you're not going to get it. I don't think any legislator is going to legislate himself out of a job.

Sibley: Well, you may be right about that. I'd like to raise another question about time. I think it's important to note, also, that in the whole process of politics, the problems which we have to solve have quite often been given to us by another generation of which we weren't members, and that we'll be passing on problems to our descendants through our legislative activity or our lack of legislative activity. Our descendants will not have been responsible for the problems that we put to them. So here you have a good example, it seems to me, of the Biblical statement, "The fathers have eaten sour grapes and the childrens' teeth are set on edge."

Adams: Well, this is true, but in many instances, public opinion is not with the political leaders. In other words, the politician doesn't want to get too far out in front in trying to lead the people. If he does, he's going to be a general without an army and he's soon not going to be re-elected. If we could somehow elevate the public so that their level of understanding of these issues was greater, I think we could move faster.

Sibley: That means we need more political education.

Adams: I agree.

Popham: I think one other important aspect of this problem of scarcity of time as it bears on the policy making process is the fact that, as our society has become increasingly complex, there's such a wealth of information that keeps coming out concerning public affairs that the average citizen is almost overwhelmed unless he spends full time reading periodicals and studying such matters. Perhaps this sometimes tends to be a little discouraging—just trying to keep up with things. On some of these complex questions like taxation, it is hard for him to know just exactly what public policy he feels would serve the ultimate good and therefore to communicate his opinion to the proper elected officials. Because he isn't certain of the consequences, he tends to oppose change. That is just the human fear of the unknown.

Sibley: This gets right into the next point, doesn't it? This whole problem of how you measure or predict consequences is very important. I just wonder whether you gentlemen have any other comments to make on it. You must come across this problem often in your activities as legislators.

Popham: Prediction, of course, is really the secret to legislating. It's easy to perceive a problem and many are those who are willing to outline what they see as a problem. What is so difficult is the ability to formulate an answer and test it by anticipation of what consequences will flow from it. This, I think, probably depends to a considerable extent on experience, which, in turn, also takes us back to time.

Hoyt: How does a practicing politician try to predict or to make short-range and long-range plans? Is it just a matter of experience, trial and error?

Adams: I think that I would have to agree that it's experience, trial and error, emphasizing the error because, being human, we are not infallible and there are plenty of times when we make errors in judgment about what we think the public will accept and will not accept. Sometimes, the public is actually ahead of the politician. In other words, sometimes the public is waiting for the politician to lead and to crystalize public opinion around a particular problem. For example, the Gallup Poll back for at least four or five years, has indicated that the public really wanted Medicare, but Medicare is not an established fact yet. You see, the legislative process lags behind. It's a matter of time. Here, again, we're talking about time and predictions. I suppose when Congressman Foran first proposed the Medicare bill about six or eight years ago, he thought it was a good solution to a real problem. Again, the lag is there. I don't know the answer.

Sibley: Well, part of the answer in this particular case was that you had a very powerful lobbying group, didn't you, on the part of one particular organization composed of a very important profession?

Popham: I don't think it's really that so much as the question of prediction. Everyone recognizes the need to aid the elderly in terms of providing medical care and treatment. The problem is to accurately predict the consequences for any one of several ways of approaching this need. Is one solution better than another? To the extent that it isn't easy to point out in a clear-cut way what is the best solution, to that extent people tend to differ.

Sibley: This reminds me of Senator Fulbright's recent statement that the settlement of the problem in Viet Nam today, which is a political problem as I guess we'd all agree, is simply a matter of time. Yet here are the long-run and the short-run again. If in the long run it's just a matter of time, what's going to happen in the short run? Thousands of people are going to be killed, possibly.

Adams: Senator Fulbright made that statement in today's paper. I noticed that he said that there probably will be a settlement after the monsoons are over. In other words, after the Viet Cong has had its guerrilla raids and has probably killed X number of men and women and vice-versa, then a settlement will come. Why can't we settle this problem before? If you're going to have a negotiated settlement, why not try to resolve it before then? It's a matter of saving face all the way around. In the Viet Nam situation, how are you going to resolve a political problem and still save face all the way around? I suppose man just isn't so rational that he can resolve these problems.

Sibley: He aspires to be rational but has not reached that stage. This is what Aristotle meant.

Hoyt: Reason doesn't exist in a vacuum. This leads to your third point, Mulford, that men must try to make his predictions and to "ratiocinate" in an environment of rapid and intense social change.

Sibley: Really, you can put it in the following way. In the old days, we can say, before the rapidity of change that we experience in modern times, habit could take care of many of these things because things didn't change very rapidly. You could build up new habits over a period of time. Now, no sooner does rapid change occur, than the problem of adjusting to it arises, and the only way that you can adjust to it is through some deliberate kind of legislative activity or political activity because you don't have time to build up new habit patterns. Yet if you don't adopt legislation deliberately, then you're subject, you see, to legislation by accident—"legislation" results from social forces, happenstance, and so on. That's implicit in this third point.

Adams: Getting back to Viet Nam, President Johnson, in a recent speech at a university, indicated that he wanted to do something specific to resolve the problem. In fact, they're referring to a TVA in that whole valley. This would resolve the conflict because the economic and political circumstances have to be resolved in this particular situation, and I hope it can be resolved this way. It's better to go out and build than to go out and continue to fight.

Hoyt: In other words, you would defend the present policy against any charge of legislation by accident because there have been proposals of rational solutions to the problem.

Adams: This has been a rational solution, it seems to me, but it's a question of whether or not both sides are willing to accept something rational at this stage of the game. It's a matter of face-saving, you see.

Sibley: If you don't save face, what does that hurt?

Adams: I have no answer to that, Mulford.

Sibley: The French withdraw from Viet Nam and they have more prestige now than they did then.

Adams: They also withdrew from Algiers.

Sibley: We all admire them for it, don't we?

Adams: I think that the question of time will resolve many of these problems but there are consequences before we resolve them.

Sibley: It's a long-run, short-run business, again, isn't it? It's very plaguing and for an active politician, such as you are, it must be particularly difficult.

Adams: Well, it becomes difficult when you know that something should be done and you are, in a way, powerless to try to resolve the problem. Public opinion resolves many of these problems, but public opinion, in many cases, is not aroused. Here is a matter of prediction. Do we know if public opinion is sufficiently aroused for the politician to move this way or that way? It seems to me that the most rapid changes that I can remember taking place were during war-time periods, during World War II in my lifetime. Many changes came about then. This was true during the depression years. Changes came about very rapidly. It is true that during the Roosevelt period the solutions that were proposed were not always good solutions but, nevertheless, there were changes being made.

Sibley: How do you account for that? Why were changes made so rapidly during that time?

Adams: I think public opinion was aroused. We were in a depression for a number of years and public opinion wanted things to be done. It didn't spell out how; that is, it didn't point the finger and say "move in that direction," but people did want to move, so FDR did move, and the Congress went along with him.

Sibley: It's frightful to think how legislation by accident would have affected the United States if some action, some deliberate legislation hadn't been made in the thirties. As a matter of fact, down in Iowa at that time there were farmers who were engaging in acts of violence against federal judges, as I recall.

Adams: This is true and not only that; they were doing it in Minnesota too— the Farmer's Holiday. We got the program of moratorium on debts during the Floyd Olson administration. There was practically a political revolution on the farms when the officers came to foreclose on the farms. So we had what we called in the thirties, the "Farmer's Holiday." I can remember that vividly—I was a student at the University at the time this happened. I don't think that was legislation by accident; it was legislation of necessity at that time.

Popham: Well, it was legislation by necessity, perhaps, but I think that there was also quite a bit of legislation by accident.

Adams: There's no question about that.

Popham: I think in many senses, our rapidity of change today is a progressively increasing matter. Population growth and the concentration of it here in our own state of Minnesota and in our Twin City area, create great problems for the legislature. The change in the economy, the inflationary trends, create problems in the policy making and in the legislative process.

Sibley: That raises the interesting question, Wayne, of whether we shouldn't try deliberately to slow up the process of change since we don't seem to be able to control it for human ends. Consider, for example, the way men are exploited through the introduction of automation—forced to change their jobs and not consulted about it, for example. Why shouldn't we halt this process deliberately and go about it more slowly?

Hoyt: In the last hundred years, surely, the economy has been marked by steady and, indeed, rapidly increasing automation. Hasn't the standard of living gone up steadily with equal acceleration? Doesn't there seem to be a correlation between the world's highest standard of living that we enjoy and the degree of automation of our economy as compared with others?

Sibley: The question I'm raising is a very fundamental one. Is the standard of living the only value we should keep in mind?

Popham: I certainly don't think that it is the only value, but the question when you are drafting legislation is how to devise a law that will apply with perfect justice to every individual. It's impossible to do because no one can predict all of the needs and circumstances of each individual, and so the law and the policies necessarily have to be general in nature. This is the political process, the need to make accommodations between conflicting groups who are competing for limited services or limited property.

Sibley: You see, one of the things that bothers me about that, though, about the whole process which you described very well, is that, if we don't do some of these things by public legislation, we in effect are turning them over to American corporate wealth to be handled by private legislation. I say "private legislation" because when the board of General Motors or the board of United States Steel operate, when they make decisions, they are acting as politicians, too. They're affecting large segments of the community in their policy making. I've been very much perturbed, too, by the enormous power of the automobile manufacturers in Congress, by the way they're exerting pressure to take off the excise tax on automobiles. The mink coat manufacturers are putting on pressure to take their excise tax off. These eliminations of taxes would come in a day when we need more public spending for public convenience.

Why do we allow so much important decision-making power to be turned over, either formally or informally, to "private" corporate enterprise?

Adams: Mulford, I want to just clue you in on something very, very important. I think that the minute Congress preempts this type of taxation, many state governments are going to be in there, taking these taxes and using them for state purposes.

Sibley: Will they be used for education and other things?

Adams: This is what we'll have to do.

Sibley: Well, I hope so.

Adams: Well, I hope so too, but I think that the state governments get into this because the states are starved in terms of appropriations. We just don't have the tax base, the tax resources that the federal government has. The city is in the same fix. Remember that the states have been dominated by rural legislators and that we are now an urban society. Minnesota, for example, was a rural state until about the mid-thirties. I think probably today figures are quoted that show about 54 to 55 per cent of the total population of the state living in the metropolitan area. We must remember that the legislative process has been dominated by people from rural areas who are not too well acquainted with urban living. Therefore, they're not as willing to spend the time and the effort to resolve urban problems.

Sibley: I take it you're opposed, then, to the proposed constitutional amendment which would overrule the Supreme Court on reapportionment and allow one house to be apportioned according to factors other than population.

Adams: Yes, I oppose that. I oppose that and this gets back to the matter of whether or not we need a bicameral legislature then. It's questionable as to whether it's necessary.

Hoyt: Mulford, time is the essence of this program. How do these considerations bear on your next point, the evolution of politics?

Sibley: It seems to me that you can't discuss politics in a vacuum and we haven't been, of course, here this evening. Does politics fit into a larger scheme of things, into a view of history, for example? Does it fit into a view of the evolution of the human race? What are we trying to do, broadly speaking, in the political arena? I would say that we're trying to develop social orders more rationally than we have in the past. That's what is implicit in the political process.

Even though we often fail miserably—the "we" including both the citizen and the legislator, as both Senator Popham and Senator Adams have pointed out—this is nevertheless the implicit purpose of the scheme. Just as we're trying as individuals, presumably, to make rational decisions and yet often fail, so politics is the process by which we're trying to order our community life rationally, although we often and perhaps mostly fail in this, too.

Popham: Well, Mulford, I didn't recall that either Frank or I ever admitted any failures on the part of the legislature.

Sibley: Maybe I read that into you.

Adams: I would agree with you on that, Wayne. I wouldn't go that far. Getting back to this question of the legislature and the planning that goes on, we do have a Metropolitan Planning Commission, and a City Planning Commission. We are planning; we are getting into this area a step at a time. Maybe we should move faster.

Sibley: We are a generation behind the need, wouldn't you agree?

Adams: Yes, maybe we should move faster.

Popham: Careful, Frank, careful—I think we were trapped here.

Adams: I do feel that the planning commissions are making a contribution toward much more orderly development of the whole community. The Metropolitan Planning Commission, for example, has made a real contribution. We don't always listen to them but, nevertheless, they are there with some well-thought-out, planned solutions for many of our growth problems.

Sibley: I agree with you, of course. I'm not suggesting that we aren't doing something. I'm just simply saying that the gap is still very great, as you yourself pointed out before.

Adams: Getting back to this same situation, you see, the planners can go out there just like the natural scientists. They don't have to deal with people. When you get into the area of social planning where you're moving people around, you get resistance. Using one specific example in a part of my district, the highway department is going to build a freeway, and the people are objecting to being moved. Now, this is something that the politician has to face. To whom do they come? They come to the politician; they object to being uprooted and so on, even though, in the long run, we're going to have better transportation.

Sibley: Are we? Can we move at all with more and more automobiles?

Adams: This is questionable, but nevertheless, we think we will. I have another solution; I want a Metropolitan Transit Authority and subways, and so on.

Sibley: We have to plan transport as a whole.

Adams: This is correct. This is where the Metropolitan Planning Commission comes in. They're making their contribution, but it is very hard to put into action what they have planned because it affects people and there's a lag here.

Hoyt: Mulford, could I just put a small question here before we move on to your next point, the "evolution of politics." It worries me just a little bit. Admitting that there are very impressive signs of progress and improvement of specific things, I wonder if the student who wants to read about political theory, who wants to ponder political ideas, would profit more from reading works of twentieth century authors than he would from reading Plato and Aristotle? I wonder if there has been any real evolution. Would you like to speak to that?

Sibley: I think that's a good question. In some respects, I think there has been some evolution and some progress. I'd have to define progress and we don't have time, I suppose, to do so; that in itself is a big order. In other respects, it seems to me, many of the problems of politics are perennial issues about which Plato and Aristotle can tell us at least as much as Harold Lasswell. There is just one final comment on this point that I really haven't had a chance to put in. It seems to me that, implicitly, in politics we're looking forward, in one sense, to a situation in which the coercion of men is to decline. In other words, we'll no longer put men in jail. I talked with a former warden at Stillwater and I asked him, "If we had a good probation system in Minnesota, how many of these prisoners could we discharge on probation?" He thought a moment and said "about ninety per cent" of them, assuming we had an adequate probation system in Minnesota. In other words, I agree with Lenin's objective—this sounds terrible, I know— that the goal, so to speak, of political activity is to eliminate the government of men, the direct coercion of men, and to make public activity primarily a matter of controlling things, material goods and so on, while only indirectly controlling man.

Hoyt: Of course, it's one thing to agree with what Lenin said and another thing to sympathize with the Ukrainians who lived under what he did.

Sibley: Oh, yes. I don't say that Lenin necessarily lived up to what he stated.

Hoyt: I'm just waiting for you to get to this next point, the assessment of legitimacy, because you made a remark which I must refer back to as soon as you come to it again. It was your reference to William the Conqueror. As I am sure students who have just taken my course know, the view you just expressed really was the Anglo-Saxon view, not the Norman view.

Sibley: That's right. It was also Tom Paine's view, of course.

Hoyt: Paine's view was popular in the eighteenth century, but a Norman of the time would have insisted that this conquest was quite legitimate—based on a legitimate claim which to him, at least, was quite rational. This was simply a case of war, force of arms, making good a just claim. So, you can't dissociate the element of might entirely from the achievement of right. Would you question that?

Sibley: That's exactly my problem. Throughout past history for the most part, might, when successful, has become right. Those who've wielded the might, of course, have claimed the right in the beginning. They say they're using the might to achieve the right as you correctly point out, but what bothers me is that so often we rationalize. If a regime stays in power long enough, we think it is righteous even though in the beginning we thought of it as unrighteous and, therefore, not legitimate. Let me raise this kind of question with you gentlemen. Why should I obey Lyndon Johnson rather than, let's say, the head of Cosa

Nostra if that organization should get control of Minneapolis and last for twenty years?

Hoyt: Isn't the element of time essential to the kind of implicit consent to government which does, after all, legitimize the government? Surely, you would say that a government by consent is legitimate.

Sibley: Well, I'm not even sure of that.

Hoyt: If there's a passage of many years during which no one objects to the government, then isn't that an expression of consent?

Sibley: That's what is often argued, of course, but I can look at the long history of the Czarist regime in Russia, for example. It was an atrocious regime.

Hoyt: But it was legitimate.

Sibley: No, I would say it was utterly illegitimate.

Hoyt: Certainly it was atrocious, but it was legitimate.

Adams: How do you define legitimacy in terms of government?

Sibley: That's what I'm trying to get you gentlemen to do for me.

Popham: It's very difficult to do. Now, you asked why you should accept the policies of Lyndon Johnson if the Cosa Nostra were in power in the city of Minneapolis. This is what you had, for example, under Hitler. Hitler was, I suppose, a legal, legitimate ruler. Yet he was a bad ruler and violence was necessary to get rid of him. I suppose to get rid of Cosa Nostra if they were running Minneapolis we'd have to resort to violence.

Hoyt: We would because they were not elected, as Hitler was.

Sibley: The United States is resorting to violence all around the world today. Does that make it illegitimate? For example, in 1954, it overthrew the legal government of Guatemala by force and violence, so that we all belong to an organization that believes in the overthrow of government by force and violence —the United States of America.

Hoyt: Well, we have since 1776, I thought.

Sibley: Surely, so what's so wrong about the Communist Party? We all belong to the same kind of an organization, if you assume that the Communist Party does indeed advocate overthrow of government by force.

Popham: What does this have to do with the question of legitimacy as related to government? What is the practical significance of the question of legitimacy?

Sibley: Well, I think the practical significance is: Ought we to obey law or rulers simply out of expediency because we fear for our necks or fear to go to jail, or do we have a moral obligation to obey certain types of governments, you see, and to disobey others? If so, what are the criteria?

Hoyt: This is why I raised the question of consent.

187

Sibley: Yes, exactly. Then, of course, you have to raise a further question, obviously: how do you know when a people are consenting? Were the Russians consenting to the Czarist rule?

Adams: This is a matter of personal conscience with each individual person. I can remember the movie that I saw on the Nuremberg trials where the generals and the Nazis were saying that they were just following the orders of their leaders. Do we continue to do this even though, in our own personal consciences, we know that the orders are bad?

Sibley: What is our obligation?

Adams: I just don't know. It's a matter of personal conscience. I think that many of the German generals, for example, were very, very sincere people. Now does this give them the right to go out there and murder millions of people?

Sibley: This problem exists in private affairs, too. The robber barons acquired their wealth in the seventies and eighties of the last century as all our American history books tell us (or most of them do), by means which were of questionable legality or morality. Many people criticized the means. However, those who managed to hold on to that ill-acquired wealth had descendants—they still have descendants in Philadelphia and New York today—and they're in the social register.

Adams: They've come to be respectable today.

Sibley: Well now, why? What gives them legitimacy now?

Hoyt: Time gives respectability.

Sibley: Well, surely, but why *should* it?

Popham: Time gives respectability through the adoption of public policies in the form of laws. The state has determined as a matter of policy that we do not confiscate wealth. However, if we chose a contrary policy, then wealth would be illegitimate.

Sibley: Much of that wealth was gained even against *the law,* not to speak of morality.

Popham: Well, I wouldn't know about that. History, of course, is written also in terms of time.

Sibley: Yes, it's written by the victors, usually.

Popham: It seems to me this question of legitimacy as it relates to politics is this: if we assume that something is immoral and therefore illegitimate, how does the mere passage of time cure this immorality?

Sibley: Exactly, you've put it very well. That's exactly what I'm asking. Now, for example, Red China has had the consent of most Chinese. At least they haven't revolted in large numbers, so far as I know, since 1949, and that's a fairly long time. Does this mean the government of Red China is legitimate? The American government says it isn't.

Adams: Maybe the Red Chinese aren't in a position to revolt just as the German soldiers weren't in a position to revolt against the Hitler regime . . .

Sibley: Or the Czarist peasants against the Czar. Most of mankind is in that condition and has always been.

Adams: This is true, but conditions, events force people into action. The revolutions just don't happen by accident. When there is much pressure and the political regimes no longer have the consent of the people, you do get these revolutions. At least, this is what history tells us.

Sibley: That's what's going on in Santo Domingo, you feel, in other words.

Popham: That would be a variety of legislation by accident.

Sibley: Yes, quite a different variety from what we were talking about before. That's a good point that you made. No, I'm puzzled about this sixth point here very much myself. That's why I'm very glad our chairman raised it explicitly.

Hoyt: Well, perhaps we should discuss legitimacy in the long-range perspective of events, which is your final point. Do you have anything to say under that final point?

Sibley: Let me take a current example. I happen to believe that the whole Communist issue today which excites so many people is a "red herring," literally, a "red herring." The major issues in politics lie elsewhere. Communism is a symptom, so to speak, of certain basic ills in the community—political, economic, and social—and we ought to be talking about those ills, primarily, and not about Communism, you see.

Adams: In many instances, I think, the Communist issue is a scapegoat. I think, in other words, people don't understand Communism, and if there's something they don't understand, they dislike it. An old expression is: "If you're not up on things, you're down on things." If you don't understand issues and you don't like the solution that is being proposed, you simply say, "Oh, that's Communism." This has no relationship to the problem involved. I just wonder if a hundred years from now our descendants won't look back on us and think, "Well, what a silly bunch of fools, talking about such an irrelevant issue."

Time, Change, and Periodization in History

Is a period of history something that exists itself or is it no more than a convenience for understanding the past?

SPEAKER: *JOHN B. WOLF,* professor of history

COMMENTATORS: *WILLIAM G. SHEPHERD,* university vice president for academic administration and formerly head of the department of electrical engineering
                               GERHARD H. WEISS, associate professor of german

Professor Hoyt: We have come finally to the discipline which is, perhaps, among all the social sciences, the most concerned with time. John, why don't you start off by telling us a little bit about just what it is that the historian deals with; what is history?

Professor Wolf: History, of course, is a lot of different things, but what the historian deals with is a rather specific and definite discipline. We make the basic assumption that there is an objective reality in the past, that things did happen in the past, that the past is real. Then we make a secondary assumption that we can find out something about this past by studying the artifacts. By "artifacts," we historians generally mean written artifacts, although we also do use other things—utensils, pictures, buildings, and the like.

History isn't what many people think it is. Many people think it is either everything that happened or *what* often happened. I suspect, as Stuart well knows, that history is what the historian *discovers* to have happened. It's the model that he makes of the processes that were going on in the past. He's interested in reconstructing a picture of some aspects of a society. He obviously cannot tell everything that happened; it would take volumes to describe what happened in any one year. However, he's not interested in what happened in a year. He is interested in the process of development of the aspects of society that he is studying.

Vice-President Shepherd: Can you tell us just how an historian would go about bringing together the facts?

Wolf: The materials? We do it in many ways. Of course, as with you scientists, no *one* person attacks the past; it is attacked by an army of men, or at least a company of men. We analyze the written records that one finds in archives to get governmental developments and military, political, and economic processes. We analyze business records, personal letters, and all sorts of written documents.

Shepherd: John, there's an enormous wealth of material, I'm sure, that the historian has to examine. How do you decide which documents are the right ones, ones which lead to the right conclusions?

Wolf: You ask two questions. You ask which are the right ones and then which are the ones which lead to the right conclusions. Some documents have to be analyzed to find whether they are authentic or not. As Stuart will tell you, many documents that the medieval historian has dealt with in the past turned out to be forgeries.

Hoyt: Sometimes the forgeries turn out to be very useful. The mentality of that period is revealed as much by what it chooses to forge.

Shepherd: How do you decide which documents are real?

Hoyt: The determination of authenticity of the documents proceeds along certain lines which have been developed under the heading of diplomatic. It's an auxiliary science. We'd be getting way off the topic to go into detail here, but, briefly, the historian *can* determine from both external and internal criticism whether or not a document is authentic, although sometimes there are borderline cases.

Shepherd: I take it that part of this is examining all the evidence and trying to see whether it has internal consistency.

Hoyt: One cannot select a useful document until one has canvassed all the available documentation.

Wolf: The point isn't so much what documents you would use. The point is the historian's assumptions about his world and what he's trying to find out about it. Like the physicist, who makes assumptions about natural forces, we make assumptions about the past, and then go back and test these assumptions. We see what evidence there is to back up the assumptions.

Professor Weiss: You must have some basis on which to make the assumptions.

Wolf: Yes, we make the assumptions because we lived in the world. Most of the assumptions that men make about their world will come out of their own experience with their own world and with the past that they have studied. In other words, we've had historians now for, say, three hundred years. They've been working on problems of history as we understand it and many, many of the assumptions we use have come out of their labors. Others come out of our own understanding of our immediate world.

Shepherd: In other words, you take advantage of all of the deductions that have been drawn in the past.

Wolf: Oh, exactly.

Shepherd: I would have disagreed with your earlier statement that you make assumptions. It sounds as though you make them on the basis of ad hoc judgments . . .

Wolf: Oh, no.

Shepherd: A scientist would take all the evidence before him and deduce a hypothesis which he'd then proceed to develop.

Wolf: It's exactly the same thing. You have behind you the work of physicists since the time of Newton, at least, and you stand on the shoulders of these people. Like you, we stand on the shoulders of the people who've gone before us in these areas. This is the only way men can make any real impact on a problem.

Hoyt: John, would you be willing to go a little further and draw the analogy with science to the point of calling history a science?

Wolf: No. I don't think history is a science in the same way physical sciences are.

Hoyt: What's the difference?

Wolf: History is a type of science. We have a scientific approach to the problem of facts. Our methodology for establishing facts is rigorous and, I think, scientific, but when we go beyond that and build a model, I think there we become social scientists, rather than scientists such as you people are, because we can't test the model.

Shepherd: The models are opinions at that point?

Wolf: As I said, history is what the historian says it is and so it *is* an opinion, but it is an opinion based upon the best evidence that an honest man can find.

Shepherd: Two historians dealing with the same facts could come out with different interpretations.

Wolf: And do sometimes. We have some very serious battles as a result of it. Then out of that comes a new conception. However, you would be surprised at how much we really do agree upon.

Weiss: This can happen even among the physical scientists.

Wolf: Oh, yes. There are differences of opinion in any discipline. This doesn't really tell much about history and time, does it. Time is another problem for the historian. Historical processes occur in time, which obviously is in the past and drops behind us.

Shepherd: In fact, without time we wouldn't have history.

Wolf: That's right. I suppose history is movement in time. It's a rather discrete time. Apparently man has been on this planet for a very long time, thousands and hundreds of thousands of years, perhaps, and maybe even longer than that. We don't really know, do we? History doesn't go back that far, for the historian doesn't accept as history events that do not allow him some contact with the minds of the men who made them. We do accept some artifacts and we're willing to go along with the archeologist and the anthropologist here and there, but by and large we insist upon having contact with the minds of the people and we are concerned with their ideas, with their conceptions of the world, as well as with a piece of their pottery.

Shepherd: As a matter of fact, you can have contact with the mind of the man who made the pottery.

Wolf: Not really, not in the real sense demanded by the historian.

Shepherd: You can observe the weapons he used.

Wolf: Yes. For example, in the Anthropological Museum in Copenhagen they have enough stone axes to equip a regiment, maybe two regiments, of stone axemen, but you do not get any real contact with the minds of the men who made them, beyond the fact that they were very clever workmen. These axes are excellent.

Weiss: Yet when you find the sketchings in the caves, you begin to feel something about the man.

Wolf: I have seen some of them; I have been in Lascaux with its wonderful paintings on the ceilings of the cave. You know that the artist was a very skillful draftsman, but what was he doing it for? Was it for the same reason that Michelangelo painted the Sistine Chapel? I doubt it, but I don't *know.* Now, if he'd written about it, perhaps I would. In other words, the word is important to the historian. The word is a reflection of man's ability to grasp and organize his world, of man's ability to make real conceptions of the objective things about him. Art tells you something, but it tells you things that you wish to make it tell. Like music, it allows you freedom. Remember, Settembrini said, "Beware of music and art. It's the *word* that one must honor as concise and real." He was right; it's the word that gives man an idea's form. Thus the historian is more interested in the written word than in the artifact. That limits him, I suppose. That means that history starts with the Egyptians.

Shepherd: Well, John, I take it that you would reject all evidence of World War II that was taken with motion picture cameras.

Wolf: Not at all. However, it can be faked. It has been; it has been faked marvelously. The camera does tell you something, but it will not tell you what words will tell. The camera will tell you nothing about how that war came about, or even how the event pictured came to be.

Shepherd: It may tell you more faithfully than the word.

Wolf: It doesn't really. It may tell you how an action was fought, but not how it came about, not why it was fought, not what men fought for or even the plan for the action. It shows men being killed and men doing things, but not why they did them. We are interested in processes, not in merely describing a fact. We wish to understand the processes by which men arrived at their social, political, economic, or intellectual forms.

Weiss: Actually isn't it the spoken word, the recorded spoken word, that is the true history then, because the written word can be interpreted in many ways, while the spoken word, through intonation and so on, has a more exact meaning?

Wolf: Of course, the historian does not have just one word; he has a series of documents. He has many words. Stuart and I both "live" in eras in which we must strive to understand what these words are about, to know, for example, what the seventeenth century man was saying. His words did not mean the same then as they do now, but we can learn what they meant. We can scrutinize available sources.

Hoyt: John, harking back to Jerry's point, wouldn't you give, if not your left arm, at least your left little finger for a motion picture newsreel of the court of Louis XIV?

Wolf: Of course I would, and I do study these things. For instance, I spent hours in the section of the Bibliothèque Nationale in which they have engravings, drawings, and etchings of the court. Indeed, not until you have seen a hunting scene of the seventeenth century do you really understand what happens at a hunt. However, this is color in my history. It is not history.

Shepherd: Well, John, let me ask you this, given your ground rules—and I'll accept your ground rules for the moment—when does history begin?

Wolf: I suppose that history begins whenever the historian starts writing about it.

Hoyt: Well, when does prehistory end and history begin?

Wolf: For my purposes I would say that the history that I know anything about as an historian began somewhere in the Tigris-Euphrates basin probably thirty-five hundred years before Christ.

Shepherd: That was when man first began to use a written . . .

Wolf: . . . or a near-written word. Of course, some of the things that we have from that period were actually written much later, but they were written from an oral tradition of the earlier period.

The history that I am interested in is the history of this modern world, this process that is making the world into one world, as we used to say back in the Second World War. It is a process of European civilization and the whole world is being affected by that process. In my opinion, this world began somewhere about 800 A.D. I like to think—Stuart and I talked about this once—that Christmas Day in the year 800 is a good place to start. Charlemagne didn't know that he was starting a new world, and in many ways he was not, but yet the crown that was put on his head can be a symbol making that day a good place for us to start. From that day, with some little back-falling—you might call the ninth century back-falling—the process that has come to make our Western civilization has continued.

Hoyt: In order to explain Christmas Day, 800 A.D., doesn't the historian have to go back a little?

Wolf: Oh, yes, of course.

Hoyt: Then, you see, you get into an endless process in order to explain what explains Christmas Day, 800 A.D. F. W. Maitland put it so beautifully when he said, "History is a seamless web. We can't cut it at any point."

Wolf: For an historian in the Middle Ages, the world by 1500 was going to pieces. The Middle Ages were waning, as the medieval historian says. However, a modern historian with the same data thinks that the world was just beginning about that time. That's what he's interested in. It depends upon the processes that interest the scholar. This is where we get periodization. For a certain process, you will say, "*This* is when it began," for another process, "*This* is when it began."

Shepherd: Right here I want to part with you because you make it sound as though the things that have made one world began only when there was a written record. Now, clearly, everything that went before influenced man's behavior.

Wolf: My point is worse than that, and I suspect that you will object. I think that this Christmas Day, 800 A.D., is as good a day as any with which to begin our one world. Stuart says you have to explain that Christmas Day; nonetheless, somewhere between the eighth and the tenth century the process that we call Western civilization gained momentum, dynamic force, whatever it is that makes the on-going process of man's existence meaningful to himself and to people afterward. It began somewhere in those years, for out of the feudal society, out of the extension of the roots that one found in this disintegrated Roman empire, the world that we have today emerged.

Shepherd: Well, you make it sound as though the world started then with all the characters appearing on the stage.

Wolf: No, I don't think that. The process that makes our world characteristically our world started then. Men were on the stage before that, but those fellows didn't make the history that I am interested in studying.

Hoyt: John, isn't the point you are making that this is a first step toward the historian's concept of periodization? There was history before 800, but the history that comes after 800 somehow is different, and therefore you can say that history can be divided. Now, if you keep going with this process, you get into more and more periods. If you're dealing with very short periods, this can become very difficult. The longer the period, the easier it is to see large-scale, long-term differences. The first division of history into periods, insofar as the Western world was concerned, was the division that is still, I think, the most commonly used: ancient, medieval, and modern.

Wolf: Stuart has said something important, something very interesting. It is a point that interests me as an historian. He divided it into ancient, medieval, and modern. According to this division, ancient history ended somewhere around the second, third, or four century. You can pick your date. Then medieval history ended with the fall of Constantinople—or with the Reformation, perhaps—and modern history began.

Now, you will remember that I said that the modern world began with 800, not with the second or fourth or sixteenth century. In other words, I am seeking a new periodization. When I went to college, we used Hays' book as a text for European history. Hays was much interested in the Reformation. He had been a convert to Catholicism and was much fascinated by the problems of the Reformation era. So he began modern history, early modern history as it was called, with the year fifteen hundred.

Shepherd: I think I begin to understand your point about history here. I would quarrel with it as a generalization, but if you want to talk about it as periodization, then I can really accept what you're talking about. You can find a corresponding situation in the sciences. We had an era when we were depending on the classical theories, but this ended with Bohr and the development of the quantum theory.

Wolf: You can see this particularly in chemistry, where after the atomic theory men began to grasp a new notion of the chemical processes.

Shepherd: I know we're on common ground at least.

Wolf: However, these periods are attempts to set up models that will explain the processes developing in the period, in a way, I think, a little different from your chemical or physical theories. They are more elastic than the chemical or physical theories have been. For instance, when I took chemistry in high school, the man —who could have known better but didn't—told us that the atom was a hard, impenetrable particle, the ultimate of matter. This is a pretty rigid idea; he taught it as the truth.

Shepherd: The point is that until the hypotheses on which the scientist is dependent fail to account for new observations, he will hold to those theories.

Wolf: The historian's problem is slightly different from this. I think our periodization is made on the basis of the historian's assumptions about his world. For instance, most modern historians writing today will put the French Revolution as a sort of watershed. I don't, and there are many of us who do not. The reason for setting the French Revolution as the watershed, the great turning point in the process of modern history, is that it was then that the bourgeois finally overthrew the regime of kings and set up a new kind of government resulting in the "liberation of man," the rights of liberty, equality, fraternity. On that assumption, you can tell the history of the Western world, the Western civilization, in terms of a rise of a class to power. My feeling about it, however, is that it is not the important thing.

I had it first brought home to me many years ago. I was with a group of Indian students, one of whom turned to me and said, "Professor, how is it that Western civilization, which in the year 1500 was certainly not the equal of ours or of Chinese civilization, today is swamping us, dominating us, changing us?" This question was a very important question in my own personal development. The same question has affected people in Europe. How is it, one asks, that Western civilization, over a period of four or five hundred years, surpassed these other civilizations? If you go back to 1450 or 1500, there were five or six civilizations in competition with each other. There was some interchange, but in general they were separate from each other. They had unique characteristic forms, and it seemed that the Westerners were certainly not the most likely to succeed. Far from it! Yet they did!

Hoyt: John, this map will illustrate the point you're making.

Wolf: This illustration was taken from a map made about 1450, and I'm sure readers won't recognize anything on it. The Mer Germanique is the Baltic, of course. At the bottom are Scandinavia, Italy, and Greece. Notice that it's all upside down. Why is it that way? It's upside down because this is the period in which Moslem civilization, in the form of the Ottoman Turk and further east in the form of the rising Moslem power in India, was in the process of winning the battle. Moslem civilization was the one which seemed to be the most likely to succeed. They were hammering at the gates of western Europe, and they had reached Vienna by 1529. A European geographer, recognizing this, drew a map of Europe, and here's how he put it. This map doesn't show it because it doesn't have the things the original map had, but he filled his map with all kinds of Moslem forms. Islam was the threat. Part of Europe was under siege from the Moslem world.

Why, then, are we not living now in an Islamic civilization—or an Oriental one for that matter? What is important in the world today is the fact that China, for instance, or Japan, adopted modern, Western, military forms, adopted modern Western military-political organization, bureaucratic organization, economic or-

ganization, social organization, educational processes. Why is this? What happened that made them do this? What I'm interested in is this world problem: Why did Western civilization impose its modes, its processes, its characteristic forms on other civilizations? This is a very important question.

The story of the rise of the bourgeoisie to power will not answer the question. The bourgeoisie rise to power led only to the liberal, democratic solution to politics.

Hoyt: John, this sounds to me as if the Western historian really has to become a world historian. History cannot be isolated in the Western part of the world.

Wolf: What we are talking about is not really world history, but rather the rise of this particular civilization of ours that has come to dominate world history.

What happened? There are two or three things. One of them is that somewhere in the seventeenth century, western Europeans learned military organization, military tactics, and produced weapons in the form of cannon and battleships superior to anything the world had ever seen before.

Shepherd: Incidentally, John, where did the cannon come from?

Wolf: I don't care where it came from originally. Who *developed* the cannon? The first man who made something means nothing. What is important is the use to which it is put. Who cares who invented them? The cannons were useful only when they began to put out a broadside of singing steel that would sink the other man's ship.

Hoyt: John, I think the latest research on this is quite interesting. Gunpowder and its use in war in the form of rockets certainly began in China long before any similar use in the Western world. The first recorded use of cannon is from the second quarter of the fourteenth century in western Europe.

Shepherd: All of your arguments so far have dealt with Western history. Now, why do you ignore all of the rest of the world?

Wolf: I do so because Western history finally dominates the rest of it. I am attempting to show what we are trying to do with periodization. A group of us are trying to point out to the world that it is not the French Revolution that has made the difference between us and other societies, but it is the rise of a state that is capable of mobilizing the military power of the community through the organization of bureaucratic and other governmental controls. Such a state was able to raise taxes, able to organize armies and navies and to control them.

Shepherd: Well, this, of course, the Chinese did, too.

Wolf: They didn't. That's exactly what they didn't do.

Shepherd: They certainly had armies.

Wolf: They weren't able to do anything with them.

Hoyt: Genghis Kahn conquered a territory three times as large as the Roman Empire.

Wolf: Certainly he did—but for how long?

Hoyt: It was not long because—in a nutshell—there was no bureaucracy, John?

Wolf: There was no bureaucracy, no way of controlling it. The other thing we are seeing that gives western European civilization its power is its new conception of matter and of force—in other words, the scientific revolution of the seventeenth century. Here is another source of strength. In other words, there are two sides to this. The one side is governmental, political, and military; the other side is scientific and intellectual. It's a new approach to the problem of matter, the world, the problem of reality.

Now, if you ask what periodization is based upon these two things, it is not the French Revolution that becomes the turning point. The French Revolution was only an episode in the process. The turning point in that process is the seventeenth century with Descartes, with Newton, with Galileo, with Fontenelle, and with the rise of the hundred-and-twenty-cannon battleship. This is the turning point in the historical process. Thus the periodization that we're trying to establish does not start early modern history with 1500 and modern history with 1789. Looking at it in this way, early modern history starts about 800 and runs to the seventeenth century. It can be called the middle ages or the early modern period. We are not in agreement about it, however. For example, there is another group of historians who look at the processes of economic development as the core of the process of change. From that point of view, the breaking point may be around 1880 with the rise of the steel-hulled ship and the universal telegraph.

Shepherd: How about the clipper ship?

Wolf: The clipper ship did not do it. It was the steel-hulled ship with a good reciprocal steam engine in it that could really carry a lot of goods and could be iced. The date is 1880.

This provides another method of periodization. The historian has troubles. They are not like your problem of conceiving the atom or some other form as the ultimate form of reality. Our problem is one of trying to approach the past, trying to discover its reality with some understanding of what we can regard as important or significant. Why is it that Western civilization is blanketing all the others, driving them into its form, forcing all societies to adopt our characteristic forms?

Weiss: I'm delighted to see that you have the same problems that we have in literary history, where at one time, learning from the scientists, we thought we could periodize everything very neatly and put little labels on it. We have found out that this doesn't work, and that there simply is no periodization. You can give some rough indications, depending on your own viewpoint, but you can never with any certainty say: this is this and it began here and ended there.

Wolf: You can if you will say what you are assuming, but the assumptions that were made in the past about historical background and historical periodization were based upon rather näive western-European-oriented ideas of man. Our present ideas are not solely western European based.

Weiss: What do you think of the whole idea of world history? What is the historian's idea of the term "world history"?

Wolf: How are you using the word "history"? If you're using the word "history" to mean did people live and did they have something happen to them . . .

Weiss: I mean the interrelationships and the happenings of nations moving and influencing each other.

Wolf: Of course, my idea, as I said before, is this: All peoples may have their own history but they're outside of world history until they come to the point at which this Western civilization, that has imposed its modes, comes in contact with them.

Shepherd: That hasn't been always true. There have been other civilizations that have been dominant.

Wolf: That's why I started at 800.

Shepherd: If you are going to use that definition of history then you're only talking about a period in history that you think is important, but you can't generalize that that's all there is to history.

Wolf: Oh exactly. This Christmas Day, 800, is where I start. You see, this leaves out very important, very interesting political, social, economic, cultural events. Nothing is more interesting than some of the things that the ancient historians have been digging out about their past, about the classical past. Egyptology, for instance, has very interesting scientific problems and has made very interesting contributions, but I have great difficulty in seeing how it is important in our own political and social organization.

Shepherd: Well, can't you argue that this is where the first real social organization occurred?

Wolf: Is that important?

Shepherd: Well, it was in Egypt where you had an abundance so that everybody didn't have to work full time for a living.

Wolf: There is a point I would like to make about that. We started our periodization with 800, you know. This would seem to say that the classical period of western Europe, the Greco-Roman civilization, had nothing to do with ours, doesn't it? Actually, as I study this period after 800, I find that first men went back to discover the theology that was developed by Greco-Roman society; then they went back and looked at the medicine developed by Greco-Roman society, and then the mathematics and finally some of the literature and so forth. Yet they adopted only that part of their discoveries that suited their own purposes. They didn't adopt the whole thing. You cannot say that Greco-Roman civilization, or Egyptian civilization, had nothing to do with European history; it has enormous things to do with it. However, it does so in that western Europeans, in the process of *their* development and for *their* needs, went out to discover what other people had known about the world, just as we did in the seventeenth century.

Hoyt: It is fair to say, surely, that the religious ceremony that constituted the coronation of Charlemagne was a product of antiquity. The government which he had at his command was the debased and deteriorated Roman provincial government. It was the only government they knew.

Wolf: It was a pretty poor carbon copy.

Hoyt: Nonetheless, it was a heritage of antiquity.

Shepherd: In that sense, John, you can say that the Chinese and Japanese are now going out to discover what the rest of the world has found.

Wolf: In a sense, that's true, but they have adopted so much of the creations of our world that it is almost that we've blanketed them. We have pushed them into these patterns. I was struck by that a year or two ago when we had a very brilliant young conductor come to visit us at the symphony, a young Japanese, one of the finest conductors we've ever had. The Japanese play Beethoven as well as we do, and they play baseball as well as we do. They do many things that are Western. Look at their towns.

Shepherd: We took on mah-jongg for a while.

Wolf: Yes, we play chess, too . . .

Hoyt: And invented chop suey.

Wolf: We have chop suey; we have a lot of things. No people live by themselves. Yet the basic process that's been developing is the process of Western civilization. It has pushed itself into people's lives, and it is on the basis of this that I try to make my periodizations. There are, let us admit, other ways of doing it, many other ways of periodizing. The historian is not like the scientist who, once he establishes that the atom is the ultimate reality, knows that's true . . .

Shepherd: Only on the basis of earlier evidence.

Wolf: At any point in time you could say they assumed these things. You're assuming things today about the world, and you *know* they're true.

Shepherd: As a matter of fact, when you write the history of a period, you write it in the context of what you have learned up to now.

Wolf: That's right, but we don't *know* that it's true.

Shepherd: Oh, no, no.

Wolf: For instance, go back and read nineteenth century scientists. They talked about these things. The atom is the ultimate thing, the ultimate reality. There's no question about it.

Shepherd: They wrote in terms of what they knew then.

Wolf: The Newtonian hypothesis about the astronomical system was the ultimate truth. Laplace knew this; he *knew* it was true. I've read him and I know that he knew it.

Shepherd: Well, I would say that it's only in terms of the evidence in hand at that point.

Wolf: Even so, he knew it was true, you see, but the historian has the problem of other historians who know it's different from the way he sees it.

Weiss: You're comparing now the modern historian with the nineteenth century scientist.

Wolf: It's more with the nineteenth century historian.

Weiss: What about the earlier historian?

Wolf: The nineteenth century historians were in the same boat. The historian has never been able to get the same kind of clean, clear-cut evidence that you people can get. You scientists can get better evidence than we can ever get. It's easier to test and you can control it. You can show that if you do this, then this and this will happen, and you can show it time and again.

Shepherd: Sometimes it doesn't happen the way you expect it to happen—and that's what leads to a departure from the old hypotheses.

Wolf: You know, the psychologists have a law that's known as Meyer's Law. Do you know what it is? Meyer's Law says that if the evidence doesn't fit the hypotheses, you throw it out.

Shepherd: Oh, now!

Wolf: Meyer was a cynical psychologist.

Shepherd: Well, now, taking this period from 800, are there subdivisions of that?

Wolf: Oh, yes, we've set up various points.

Hoyt: Isn't it true, John, that ideas or attitudes or men's political or economic achievements are not the only criteria for periodization on the short range? For example, in literature, in art, in daily habits, in the way people work, in all sorts of ways, things change. These changes may be significant or perhaps even not significant, as for example in costumes, in what people wear. I think this is a beautiful illustration of periodization.

Wolf: Yes, here's a costume of the ninth century which is what they were wearing on that Christmas Day, I suppose. It was cold.

Hoyt: It shows a great Germanic contribution—long pants. You never saw a Roman in long pants; he wore a toga.

Wolf: He didn't need it—although long pants could be used in some parts of Italy. The thirteenth century man still wore the long pants, but he's changed them a bit. The fifteenth century costume has changed again. These are French designs, I think.

Hoyt: Notice, incidentally, the increase in the standard of living as illustrated from the thirteenth to the fifteenth century. Costume becomes much more elaborate, much more expensive.

Wolf: Of course, I think maybe our pictures are taken of different classes of people, too, because the thirteenth century was quite prosperous.

Hoyt: They didn't dress as fancily in the thirteenth.

Wolf: Maybe not. Here's the time that they began to dress fancily, the sixteenth century with Francis I in France.

Weiss: That's a fascinating period in German literature because quite a bit of German literature deals precisely with those very elaborate pants. They caused many complaints. They are interesting historical documents.

Wolf: These illustrations are very interesting and revealing.

Shepherd: I take it some of these costumes show that people really didn't have to work, because the clothes are not very utilitarian.

Wolf: That's right. These people fought; they were soldiers.

Hoyt: They didn't fight in those clothes.

Wolf: No, not in these clothes. However, our soldiers don't fight in the clothes they wear on parade, either, do they? This is parade clothing. The illustration shows Louis XIII and Louis XIV. Louis XIV had already begun to make the court quite important. They weren't fighting any more. In the eighteenth century a look of elegance emerged. In the first part of the seventeenth century, men developed the big, flowing wigs and the big flowing beards, and from that period on you see them clipping the wigs and clipping the beards. By the eighteenth century both of them are very close. In the nineteenth century most all of it disappears.

Hoyt: Then the process was reversed.

Wolf: Well, then we have beards, but we do not have wigs.

Hoyt: Yet, in the mid twentieth century we're back to wigs—for women.

Wolf: I guess some men are wearing wigs. Now here's your bourgeois coming to power. Many historians used to think that when this occurred the world was right. Guizot wrote, for instance, that the whole history of the Western world was explainable only in terms of the rise of the bourgeois to power, and once that happened, history could stop. Well, Marx, you know, went him one better with the rise of the proletariat; then history could stop. Here, this is also bourgeois. This is the bourgeois empire. This is Louis Philippe at 1830-1848— a very amusing costume. The last is modern.

These costumes could be used to describe history. You could use them to show characteristic patterns, but if you do, you are not looking at history in the way I'm suggesting we should, namely that we should see history as the largest possible process. The historian is trying to find the important processes that are occurring in the world and how they developed. He may not really find them, the world is much more complex than we like to believe.

Shepherd: History in this view is a force for social change. Is this it?

Wolf: It studies change. We have to study the process of change. I've suggested to some of my students that history should be part of the biological sciences. History is really the study of the human mind in the process of time, and the human mind

is a biological phenomenon. The rise of this human mind in the last five or six thousand years is the most amazing thing that's ever happened on this planet.

Shepherd: John, let me ask you another question that certainly a scientist would ask himself after he had deduced or developed hypotheses to explain the phenomena that he had observed. He would then go on to try to predict other things. Does the historian attempt to predict the future?

Wolf: That is why I say we can't do what you people can do.

Shepherd: Why not?

Wolf: We know a lot about the world. We can make wise guesses but we're very often wrong.

Weiss: You can't say that you are learning a lesson from history?

Wolf: No, I do not see it so. I think the historian does learn a great many things and that people can gain wisdom from history, but I do not believe they can gain the ability to predict. You can gain insight into processes, insight into movements, insight into the way things happen. That's what we teach our students. We teach them to recognize the forces and the processes of change. We also teach them that they can't understand them all.

The development of the atomic bomb, for instance, came from a series of events completely unrelated to the political structure of western Europe and still, it is the most important, the most significant factor in our political society today. In the year 1938, one could not have foreseen this, and still, look what has happened. In other words, the historian is confronted always with the fact that his evidence allows him to have wisdom, perhaps, but not assurance about anything.

Shepherd: What you're saying is that in contrast to the scientist, who would try to forecast what would happen in the light of what he had learned, you have less control over the variables.

Wolf: Exactly. What we can do and what I think the historian should do, is to try to teach people who are going to be statesmen and who are going to control politics and other things, to have understanding of the processes at work in the world. In other words, they should know how political entities function, what they have done in the past. They should also know that they're not going to function in the future in just the same way.

Charles de Gaulle is a good example of a person using this kind of analysis. He analyzes his world on the basis of the historical past, and on the basis of a very keen and very intelligent observation of that historical past. He also uses other things. However, his development of the Franco-German alliance, his acceptance of the whole process of Common Market and the other European agencies, as well as his attempt to set up France's role in this new world—these are all based on his interpretation of history and on analysis of the historical past, in which he tries to understand how various peoples have functioned in the past and to project their functioning into the future. He knows that he cannot really project what's going to happen, but he can understand much about *how* they're going to behave by what they have done in the past.

Shepherd: Well, so you really *do* try to predict the future, taking into account new variables that you can foresee.

Wolf: I use that word "wisdom"; it's a better word than "prediction." The historian can help people to project themselves into the future, but this projection is an act of will, not of scientific accuracy. It's an act of will and imagination to project yourself, your people or your society into the future structure. You know that you cannot be completely right. You have to accept the fact that there are many forces you do not understand. The world is terribly complex. The simplicity with which some of our political leaders explain the world to our citizens just makes my hair stand on end. There is often a näivete about the way we approach our world that shows we just do not understand its complexities. I think you'll agree with this, won't you, Stuart?

Hoyt: Well, I don't know. I think this is a very interesting hypothesis. The historian is concerned with the future as anyone else is, but only to the extent that anyone else is, not as a professional historian. Yet, as a professional historian, he must project himself into the past. Before the program began, you were using a very interesting phrase, "psychological time."

Wolf: Yes, I want to turn to that. I think our professor of German will be interested in that, too. I don't know whether it is sound or not, but it is interesting. If we go back to the period of Louis XIV, which is the one I'm interested in, we find ourselves with an understanding of some of the things that happened both before and after. We try to project ourselves into *his* life, into his existence, and there time becomes an entirely different thing. You are inside of a past that you know is going in a certain direction. Thomas Mann does this beautifully in the "Joseph" volumes.

Weiss: Yes, of course. In any case, I think it is the work of the poet to penetrate the mind of the past and then stay there and look forward as well as backward as Joseph does, of course.

Wolf: We call this "creative reconstruction" among historians.

Weiss: The trend in modern literature in general is that you very often start at the end of the historical process and then work your way back into it. Troy is already destroyed and then you go back into it and find out what happened as best you can.

Wolf: The other thing that we were talking about is also shown by Thomas Mann, who is one of my favorite writers, in the *Magic Mountain.* He has Hans Castrop come to the mountain, and the first two or three weeks of Hans' stay in a sanatorium take up over half the book, while the last five years is done in about twenty to thirty pages. An historian does the same thing, only in reverse. The historian recognizes that the immediate past is a much richer and much more important past to each one of us than the more remote past, and so as we study the past, we present it to students and readers and even to ourselves almost like an inverted pyramid. The base is very broad—that's the very recent past—and then the pyramid drops into the most distant past. We know very little about what happened to Amenhotep III, you know, or very little about what happened to Charlemagne, actually.

Weiss: Isn't here also where the literary element—for example, a contemporary novel—comes in very strongly? At any time in history, a contemporary dealing with the problems of the time sees them in such a way as the time saw them and gives you historians an insight which you otherwise could not get.

Wolf: That's right. I could not have written one of my books without Zola and Balzac. They were terribly important to me because they gave me psychological insights into mid-century France.

Weiss: I always require of my students that they read certain post-war German novels which captured the time much better than any statistics. If I tell them of refugees or of soldiers returning from prisoner-of-war camps, that doesn't do it, but if they read Borchert's *Thousand Draussen vor der Tür* or a play of that sort, they are *in* the time.

Wolf: That's right. The historian finds that always. You asked if we use only the written word. Of course, we don't. I spend a lot of time in art galleries looking at pictures and sculptures because illustrations do give you insights, too. However, those insights, I think, are dangerous, and, for an historian, treacherous unless he has the written word to go with them.

Hoyt: You can write history with the written word minus pictures, but you can't write history with pictures minus the written word, even though pictures can be very helpful.

Wolf: They're terribly important.

Weiss: However, you don't only use pictures. You can, of course, use peculiar myths about history.

Wolf: A nice example of this is the series that Rubens did for Marie di Medici in the Louvre. You can see them in the Rubens Room. They start with the birth of Marie di Medici and finally reach the rebellions. Of course it tells a marvelous story but it did not happen that way. It is the way that Marie di Medici wanted the story to be told and Rubens didn't care whether it was right or not. He wanted to make a good picture and as dramatic a picture as he possibly could. They're good pictures, but bad history.

Shepherd: Would cartoons help the historian?

Wolf: Oh, of course they do.

Shepherd: There are marvelous cartoons in Prado in Madrid.

Wolf: Do you know that we are so well served here in the Twin Cities with Roy Justus and Scott Long as cartoonists that you could write a marvelous history of Twin Citians' attitudes about the world and things that happened, just from their cartoons. Still, I think you'd probably get a warped notion of what happened in the mid-twentieth century. They're superb, but you have to use other things, too. Without the word, as you say, Stuart, they wouldn't be enough.

Hoyt: Well, John, can you sum up for us? What is periodization for the historian?

Wolf: Periodization is many things. It really depends upon what the historian assumes he's working upon. If he assumes he's working on the rise of a class, then he does one thing with his periodization. If he assumes he's working on a religious problem, he'll do another thing with it. If he assumes he's working on an economic problem, he'll do another thing. If he assumes he's working on this big problem that I suggest is important, which is the question of why one civilization finally triumphed over others, then he does something else with it. In other words, periodization is based fundamentally upon the assumption that the historians make about what his task is. Then he will make the periods on the basis of the best information he can get from his and other historians' studies of that past.